The Rhino Man and Other Uncommon Environmentalists

Cover photo: Amazon forest in the vicinity of Rio Branco, Brazil. The forest is frequently burned to create grazing lands for cattle. The land remains fertile for only a few years, at which time more forest is cleared. In the past decade, ten percent of the Amazon forest has been destroyed. (Photograph © by Mark Edwards/Still Pictures.)

The Rhino Man and Other Uncommon Environmentalists

Winthrop P. Carty
and
Elizabeth Lee

Population Reference Bureau

Seven Locks Press
Washington, DC

96 95 94 93 92 6 5 4 3 2 1

Manufactured in the United States of America

This book is set in 11-pt. Palatino and printed using a soybean-based ink, on acid-free, recycled paper.
Cover design by New Age Graphics, Bethesda, MD
Cover photograph © by Mark Edwards/Still Pictures, London, UK
Printed by Kirby Lithographic, Arlington, VA

Library of Congress Cataloging-in-Publication Data
Carty, Winthrop P.
The rhino man and other uncommon environmentalists / by Winthrop P. Carty and Elizabeth Lee.
p. cm.
ISBN 0-9631509-0-1
1. Conservationists — Biography. 2. Environmentalists — Biography. 3. Wildlife conservationists — Biography. 4. Nature conservation.
I. Lee, Elizabeth. II. Title.
QH26.C28 1992
333.7'2'0922—dc20 92-9166
CIP

Seven Locks Press
3030 Clarendon Blvd., Suite 202
Arlington, VA 22201
(703) 243-1280

Contents

Foreword

The United Nations Environment Program's annual Global 500 award series began in 1987 as a modest attempt to cite a finite number of individuals and organizations for outstanding achievements in protection and improvement of the environment. The Global 500 Roll of Honor has grown into something more than an award for the chosen few; it now stands as a challenge to us all to emulate the laureates.

The award winners come from all walks of life, from every social and economic stratum, from all races, creeds, and ideologies and speak all manner of languages. The stories of the individual laureates are instructive and entertaining. But collectively they tell one essential truth: everybody—and I do mean everybody—can and must contribute to the repair of our planet.

International agencies may hold conferences, governments may make laws, and august figures may issue proclamations, but ultimately the fate of the global environment will be determined by average men, women, and children modifying their daily pursuits.

We have discovered that humanity is at war with its environment. Thoughtlessly, we have allowed ourselves to believe that nature is something to be conquered, and we are measured by our ability to consume. *The Rhino Man and Other Uncommon Environmentalists* illustrates how a variety of world citizens and organizations have bypassed conspicuous consumption in favor of a more environmentally sensitive way of life.

Virtually all of the Global 500 laureates are exceptionally well motivated, most are highly effective in their particular realm, and a few are truly heroic. How are we going to meet the challenge of their example? Our collective answer very well could determine the future of life on Earth.

Mostafa K. Tolba
Executive Director
United Nations Environment Program

Preface

The story of the Global 500 laureates is really the story of environmentalists everywhere. These hard-working individuals and organizations singled out by the United Nations Environment Program (UNEP) for extraordinary environmental achievement represent countless other concerned and committed citizens around the globe who struggle on for the sake of the Earth.

When UNEP began the Global 500 Roll of Honor in 1987, its intent had been to name 100 winners each year for a period of five years, thus reaching the award's namesake number. As the criteria for winning were tightened, however, UNEP named fewer winners each year. At the same time, response to the series was highly positive. So UNEP has extended the Global 500 indefinitely. Due to timing, we do not cover the 1992 winners in this book, except to list them in the complete roster of laureates in the closing pages.

In selecting the winners—who receive their certificates on World Environment Day, on or about June 5th of every year—UNEP has tried to maintain a balance among income levels, geographic regions, and religious, age, and ethnic composition. The result is a richly diverse group of awardees whose views and backgrounds are often at odds. As a category, only the purely political laureates—usually the heads of state—are of questionable merit. On the other hand, three laureates have been martyred, and many others have been jailed, ostracized, fined, or exiled because of their actions.

In putting the book together, we focused on the uncommon environmentalists—individuals who demonstrate that we all can do something if we only try. The much-needed recognition—and, in some cases, protection—that the award lends to grassroots environmentalists is, in our minds, the strength of the Global 500 process. Of course, in focusing on the grassroots winners, we exclude many worthy laureates such as those in the world of academia, influential international institutions, and philosophical pursuits. Time and money alone set the limits of this book; there are many exceptional winners in places we were unable to visit, such as the Middle East and Eastern Europe, who could have filled a whole volume by themselves.

But while we could not interview all the winners, and some information had to be gathered second-hand, we are confident that the book—written in complete independence of its funders—provides an accurate snapshot of the overall group.

Of the laureates we did interview, we found that the vast majority are highly motivated, not by desire for fame or fortune, but by a vision of a better world. Winning the UNEP award may be their only connecting thread, but collectively the laureates represent some of the world's best environmental activists.

Gathering information on the far-flung winners over the past two years has been an adventure. We have chatted with a laureate on a houseboat on the Tiber River in Rome, toured a rhino outpost in a Kenyan national park, trudged along a dirt trail to find an awardee in the hills of Indonesia, scrambled among the ruins of the Acropolis with the man determined to save the remaining Greek monuments, captured the aspirations of a tree planter on a small Kenyan island in Lake Victoria, been inspired by a Buddhist monk on a ridgetop in Thailand, listened to a photographer give voice to his vision over the din of a London pub, mucked through Kathmandu's muddy streets, dodged hair-raising traffic in Cairo, and watched laureates receive their awards in Mexico City and Stockholm.

We have viewed numerous television videos, made countless telephone calls, and written to every living laureate in the world at least once. In all, we have spoken with more than sixty laureates from Africa, North America, Asia, Europe, and Latin America.

We became involved in the Global 500 award process as journalists reporting on UNEP's activities. The more we learned about the award winners, the more we were inspired to continue our own work, and it is our hope that *The Rhino Man* passes on that inspiration to all who read it.

This book calls for many acknowledgments. Alcoa of Australia, a 1990 Global 500 laureate, provided the lion's share of the funding, and the company's genial Public Relations Manager, Brian Wills-Johnson, insisted that we write the book as we saw fit. The U.S. Alcoa Foundation also contributed funds to the project. UNEP's Executive Director, Dr. Mostafa K. Tolba, graciously provided our foreword. UNEP's Information Director, Tore Brevik, and its former Coordinator of External and Organization Communications, Daniel Kinnear, were stalwarts throughout the undertaking. James McGrath Morris of Seven Locks Press was supportive from the word go. Phil Noyce, with the Australian Commission for the Future (a 1989 Global 500 laureate), provided valuable assistance with mailing lists of all the winners. Fellow employees Sasha Loffredo and Nancy V. Yinger at the Population Reference Bureau—a nonprofit, demographic, educational institution—reviewed the manuscript, as did Dr. Richard Haeuber, an independent environmental consultant.

But we are most grateful for the outpouring of help we received from the laureates themselves. In person, by telephone, and by letter they shared with us their stories and their dreams. We finished this project with the impression that despite the many challenges we face, there is hope for the Earth after all.

1

Noah's Children

Some Global 500 laureates are motivated to protect an animal because its possible extinction represents the destruction of the surrounding habitat, the loss of a precious way of life, or a threat to the planet.

> *The animals ask*
> *If we spoke your language,*
> *Would you listen to us?*
> *Would you understand*
> *What we animals have to say?*
> *Or would you remain deaf,*
> *Still pretending not to hear?*
>
> *Hearing, as you well know,*
> *Requires more than just*
> *A pair of ears.*
> *If you refuse to open*
> *Your mind and your heart,*
> *Words will not reach you,*
> *And speaking your tongue*
> *Will be of no avail.*
>
> *Did not the slaves speak*
> *The language of man?*
> *Did not the serfs, the Indians, the Jews*
> *And whoever were*
> *The subhumans of the day*
> *Beg you in human tongues*
> *To spare them torture and death?*
>
> ***—Godofredo Stutzin,***
> ***Global 500 laureate***

Other laureates are driven by a simple love of animals. The most extreme case is Parbati Baruah, an Indian princess who devotes her life to protecting wild elephants. The quixotic woman reportedly leads a nomadic life deep in the forests of the Himalayan foothills.

A Reuters correspondent caught up with Baruah a couple of years ago while she was helping drive a herd of wild elephants to the security of a deep forest. He wrote: " 'I love the forest and the elephants. This is my kind of life and I want to live it this way,' says the diminutive aristocrat, standing confidently between the huge legs of a cow elephant. She dabs lotion on a wounded elephant and croons softly as it wraps its trunk around her. Villagers watch and gape.

While Baruah has no formal education in wildlife management, her way with elephants is legendary. Her husband is another matter: "The last time I met my husband was after an absence of eighteen months, and that was for about two hours. I don't know how to put this to you—but bluntly my husband and my family are less important. I live for my elephants."

In many ways, laureate Vivian J. Wilson is quite the opposite of Baruah. A scientist who has published more than fifty papers on herpetology, mammalogy, and ornithology, he is recognized as a world authority on the duiker, an endangered small African antelope. And he has had a long career as a habitat manager. What he does share with Baruah is a love of animals.

Wilson, a rugged Zimbabwean known as Viv, was born in Johannesburg, South Africa, in 1932. As a young man he was interested only in wild animals and wide-open spaces. He traveled in southeast Africa in an unsuccessful quest for a park ranger's job. The story of his search made the local newspapers and in 1954 resulted in a post at the Umfollozi Game Reserve in South Africa. Subsequent assignments in an adventuresome career took him to what are now Zambia and Zimbabwe.

As a ranger, he had the task of killing animals if they became sick, disease-carriers, or overabundant, posing a threat to humans and their farms. In his autobiography, *Orphans of the Wild,* Wilson described his reaction to having to shoot his first elephant:

"What a pitiful sight to see such a vast mass of what had been living flesh, now lying dead. Though I comforted myself with the fact that I had carried out my instructions, I was nauseated by the need to destroy such a magnificent animal. It had lived for dozens of years to reach its size, only to be felled in a split second by a single bullet."

As he became a more senior game park warden with the increasing authority to exercise his personal judgment, Wilson began taking in wild orphans. At his animal nursery in Chipangali, Zambia, he found the feeding and rearing of the babies a heartrending matter of trial and error, all too often resulting in their death despite exhausting attempts to save them. Wilson swallowed his disappointment and continued his effort to rear baby animals until they could be returned to their natural habitat.

Returning animals to the wild is another heartrending matter of trial and error, Wilson discovered. Semi-tame animals on their own are not sufficiently wary of humans and can end up in the village cooking pot, have trouble learning how to feed themselves, or become the easy prey of other animals. Some orphaned animals become too dangerous or destructive and have to be destroyed.

Another problem for Wilson is the attachment he develops for the wild animals he rears. Wilson equates the bond with the love any owner has for a pet kitten or puppy nursed back to health.

Chaka, a leopard cub, was one of Wilson's more challenging wards. From a seven-pound cub, he quickly grew into a beautiful and unpredictable animal. The young cat's play was rough, often drawing blood from Wilson. Despite the leopard's dependence on his keeper and the man's love for his adopted animal, the impossibility of keeping such a wild beast soon became apparent when Chaka mauled a park staff member. "I had no choice but to destroy the leopard," Wilson recalled, "although I loved him."

Jenny, a baby elephant found guarding the body of her dead mother, was another favorite. She became absolutely tame, trumpeting with delight when Wilson squeezed her. Jenny would barge into Wilson's quarters and plop down on the floor to sleep. Prone to illness, she caught pneumonia one day and quickly died.

"She was so gentle and so lovable," Wilson wrote in his autobiography. "She left a great gap in our lives. . . . It is hard to believe that people can become so deeply attached to an animal. The news of Jenny's death soon spread among the area people and hundreds called to say how sad they were. Many brought live chickens and green mealies as tokens of sympathy."

In 1965, Wilson was posted in preindependence Zimbabwe, and his reputation as a wild animal caretaker came with him. Many people find that making a pet of a young jungle beast is more than they bargained for when it begins to grow up, and increasingly Wilson was given the task of caring for unwanted pets as well as newborns whose mothers had died or abandoned their offspring in the wild.

Wilson's tragicomic tale of a baboon's misadventure perhaps best illustrates the unforeseen complexities of returning a semi-tame creature to its natural state. To obtain a pet, a man shot a mother baboon and took her newborn. At first the little short-tailed

George Archibald, a Global 500 laureate, dances with Gee Whiz, a whooping crane. The whooping crane's return from the brink of extinction is one of the most encouraging stories in conservation. (Photograph by David H. Thompson)

monkey made a great pet, beloved by its owners. As it grew, it became more and more dangerous, dirty, and destructive.

Wilson was given instructions by the park service to release the baboon on a ranch. He drove to a spot in the bush to give the animal its freedom. Terrified at being left on its own in the wild, the baboon chased after Wilson, jumped back into the vehicle, and clung desperately to his neck. "When I tried to pull it off," Wilson related, "it urinated and defecated all over my clothes and neck." Wilson drove back to town with the attached monkey.

Forewarned by Wilson's experience, another man was able to unload the baboon at a beautiful spot out of town. The next day, however, two unwary tourists, a man and his wife, stopped their car in the area. Starved for human security, the baboon jumped into the car and got a death grip on the woman's neck. Fearful of being bitten, the horror-stricken woman had to be taken to the police station to be separated from the clinging baboon. The wrenching cycle was completed when the baboon was destroyed for being a pest in polite society.

In 1972 Wilson was made the Director of Bulawayo's splendid Natural History Museum, a must-see attraction for any visitor to Zimbabwe's second largest city. The same year he married his wife, Patricia Ann, or Paddy. And later he purchased a large spread of land—forty hectares—outside of Bulawayo where he could take his collection of animals and establish the Chipangali Wildlife Orphanage, named after the district where he happily served as a park ranger in Zambia.

The orphanage is an extremely clean and well-equipped facility. The Wilsons' living quarters, administration buildings, and laboratory are capped with thatched roofs. "I try to keep the place African," Wilson explained to us. "It blends in with the environment." The orphanage was designed by Paddy, who is very much a partner in the Chipangali enterprise.

The ten-hectare orphanage is well-kept by a staff of nearly fifty. Visiting scientists go about their measurements and notetaking, while tourists walk the area to observe the animals. Paddy, who has reared many of the animals, can call an orphan to the side of the pen to affectionately scratch its ear, but during our visit we were cautioned to keep our distance. The lions, cheetahs, and the beautiful small cats—caracals, servals, and black-footed cats—are attractive but unapproachable. "Cats bite," Wilson warned us, holding up the stump of an index finger that was bitten by a lion.

The Wilsons hope that people will pay something toward the care of animals that they bring to Chipangali as an ongoing responsibility. "We hope others will 'adopt' an animal." The orphanage is run as a nonprofit trust and receives private and government support. In addition to the attention brought to it by Viv Wilson's autobiography, Chipangali was the subject of a thirteen-part television series featured in the United States.

"We don't want a zoo," Wilson said. The Chipangali Wildlife Orphanage serves a variety of functions, including a place to practice veterinary medicine, research animal behavior, breed endangered species in captivity, train animals for a return to the wild, and keep unreturnable orphans.

"Most big cats can't go back," Wilson explained, pointing to a young lion that will remain in the orphanage. "We will only try to introduce a captured cheetah, for example, to areas where there are not other cheetahs." Monkeys, accepted on an individual basis, must first be integrated into a cohesive group at Chipangali and then released together in a carefully chosen spot. The diet of the monkeys at the orphanage must replicate what will be available to them on the outside.

As a scientist and wildlife manager, Wilson knows that love alone will not save Africa's animals. "The saving of the wildlife must come from black people. They must see the value of the animals, if for no other reason than for the protein. The trouble with the old colonial national parks was they were never of any value to the people.

"Urban Africans are growing up with no more knowledge of wildlife than people in London or New York. You cannot ask people to save something they have never seen. Chipangali shows people what they have."

Global 500 laureate Lily Charamis Venizelos is as determined to save the Mediterranean sea turtle as Parbati Baruah is to save the elephant. But Venizelos' approach to saving her ward represents a different vision.

We met with Venizelos in Athens during the month of August. Normally in the hot summer season she would be in her London apartment or on the move in Europe. In her flat near the ruins of the

Acropolis, she outlined for us the circuitous route that brought her to her species-saving mission.

At her family's summer home on the island of Hydra, young Lily Charamis, the daughter of an eminent Greek eye surgeon, found nature an escape from family problems. She identified with the creatures of the island, even to the point of releasing her father's hunting dogs to protest his sport of shooting birds.

After her marriage to Lefterio Venizelos, the grandson of one of her country's most notable statesmen, she led the privileged and predictable life of an international socialite. She learned to speak English and French fluently, traveled widely, and enjoyed snorkeling and shell collecting.

In 1974, a storm in the Ionian Sea forced her yacht to find safe haven in Zakynthos Island's Laganas Bay. She later swam to shore and found "a paradise of birds, wild flowers, trees, and an enormous pristine beach. I thought I was in a dream. Somehow, I felt there was a message there that I had to discover."

In search of the message, Venizelos returned repeatedly to Laganas Bay, only to find that bulldozers and workers were converting her paradise into beachfront hotels. One day in a dentist's waiting room she casually picked up a magazine and read that Laganas Bay was a crucial nesting place for the *Caretta caretta*, or loggerhead, turtle. The magazine article contended that the very survival of the sea creature was in doubt. Venizelos had discovered Laganas' message: the sea turtles had to be saved.

> *We live amid a ferment of convern over humanity's future on this, our "only one earth." Around us, we see the global climate and environment—systems so vast that they dwarf us as human individuals—being disturbed and damaged by our collective actions. We see species and ecosystems that have endured for millions of years waning towards extinction. We see social and economic turmoil and deep desire for reconstruction that brings harmony between humanity and nature. We fear that time is running out.*
>
> ***—Martin W. Holdgate***
> ***Director General of the International Union for Conservation of Nature***
> ***Global 500 laureate***

From an elegant dilettante, she became a single-minded environmental advocate on behalf of the loggerhead. But the opposition is formidable, too. Mankind's expanding realm clears the elephant's stomping grounds, fills the swampy way stations of migratory birds, and cuts down the forest habitat of millions of living things. Unspoiled beach-front property around the world is under intense pressure from developers who can make a sure profit building resort facilities for an expanding world population.

In 1988, Lily Venizelos founded the Mediterranean Association to Save the Sea Turtle, MEDASSET, aimed at protecting the Laganas Bay nesting area. "We can still save the turtles," she argued, "if we care enough." She played on Greek pride and sentiment: the loggerhead turtle, one of the world's oldest species, is a "wronged animal" because it is not cuddly like the panda; ancient Greek coins dating back to 500 B.C. bear the turtle's likeness; will we allow animals that have survived since the time of dinosaurs to be eradicated by beach chairs and discotheques?

As is the case for virtually all single-issue environmental advocates, she discovered that her beleaguered ward's problems go beyond the challenge of the developers. The sea turtles are also threatened by fishermen's illegal drift nets and incidental entrapment by long line hooks intended for swordfish and tuna. Overexploitation in some of the Mediterranean's many jurisdictions is also depleting marine stocks.

Pollution of the sea is yet another threat. Floating plastics, mistaken for jellyfish, a favorite meal, can block the turtle's digestive tract. Young turtles can be made so buoyant by consuming plastics that, unable to dive for food, they starve.

In her crusade, the dynamic fifty-six-year-old woman discovered that the sea turtle was mysterious and really little was known about it. A lack of scientific knowledge was a barrier to finding solutions, so MEDASSET expanded into research. It is now studying such areas as the turtle's nesting grounds, migratory routes, patterns of movement, and the whereabouts and deterioration of wintering and foraging grounds.

Tirelessly, Venizelos attends international conferences, raises money for MEDASSET, lobbies governments, holds press conferences, addresses interested groups, and uses her international social standing to press the loggerhead's cause to European leaders. From a personal cause largely financed by Venizelos, MEDASSET has gained international acceptance and scientific recognition, including support from the European Community.

Laganas Bay, the original impetus, is still her biggest battle. Marine turtles are classified as an endangered species, and the Mediterranean Sea holds the special dangers of a heavily exploited and enclosed body of water. The once-isolated beach on Laganas Bay is a key nesting area for the loggerhead. Annually about 800 or 900 females emerge from the sea in the dark of night and drag their heavy bodies (up to 125 kilos) onto the beach, dig a hole with their back flippers, and lay their eggs.

The construction of beachfront hotels creates a variety of problems for nesting turtles. Venizelos complains that existing laws to protect the loggerhead simply are not enforced. The "selling of sun and sand on the cheap," she contended, has created a headlong rush of destruction. "As a result of illegal beachfront development," she said, "including sea walls, noise and light in the evening, vehicles, sun umbrellas and deck chairs on nesting beaches, and propeller-powered speed boats, out-of-control tourism disturbs, disorients, frightens, and injures turtles and prevents them from nesting." The same process, she adds, is happening in Turkey and other Mediterranean countries.

Venizelos ceaselessly raises hell about humanity's encroachment on the turtles' ancient nesting grounds. "It has been said," she told us, "that I make a good friend and a bad enemy." But can she stop the developers? It is a problem faced by environmentalists around the world who are trying to protect the world's dwindling area of waterfront lands needed for marine life.

Although Lily Venizelos is called the "Turtle Woman," she does not romanticize the sea creature. She has stationery, jewelry, and household items that carry a turtle image, but she has never seen the Mediterranean loggerhead in the wild and has said, "I refuse to impose my presence on their beach, even in the least disturbing way." It is enough for her to know that the ancient animal, which shares her disappearing paradise, is endangered.

2

Rare Birds

A bird in flight seems so free that it is hard to imagine it as dependent on a specific habitat. But many birds are, and their fate may well rest in the work of today's bird-watchers—rare birds in their own right.

Paul Butler, a 1989 laureate, is so associated with saving the St. Lucian parrot, a handsome blue, red, and green bird, that Caribbean islanders often call him "Paul Parrot" or "Paul Jacquot," using the patois name for the once-endangered *Amazona versicolor*.

Butler cuts the figure of an eccentric. He is lean, long-haired, nervous, and driven. He has, without question, evolved a most effective campaign to save the birds and forests of St. Lucia. His techniques are now being adopted by many of the neighboring island nations of the Caribbean. The St. Lucian movement, he stresses most emphatically, was fashioned in partnership with his close personal friend, Gabriel L. Charles, the former Chief Forest and Lands Officer of St. Lucia and himself a Global 500 laureate.

We met with Butler when he visited Washington, D.C., to address a meeting of conservationists. One of the first things we wanted to know was if he had a particular fondness for the St. Lucian bird. "I caress my wife, not a parrot," he shot back. Similar to some other Global 500 winners, the thirty-five-year-old British-born wildlife biologist has come to see his adopted ward as the symbol of and solution for the larger problem of habitat destruction.

Butler, a graduate of England's Northeast London Polytechnic, led a group of British biology students to St. Lucia in 1977 to study the problems of the bird. While they found some parrots were killed in attempted captures for pets or for sale on the international market, the team determined that the main threat came from the destruction of the forests as the island population grew. "I found," he said, "that it was at the moment more important to take action than to be a scientist. You cannot change people's attitudes by measuring the length of the parrot's egg."

After his initial survey, Butler, much to his surprise, was called back in 1979 to help Gabriel Charles work up an awareness program to protect the parrot and its vital habitat. Butler and Charles knew that the parrot's forest home was disappearing at the rate of 2 percent annually.

When St. Lucia obtained independence in 1979, the *Amazona versicolor* was named the national bird. Butler and Charles pegged an islandwide conservation program on the colorful bird. Islanders were reached through churches, schools and assemblies, newspapers, lectures, slides, radio and television, posters, reggae music, and billboards. The message was simple: the *Amazona versicolor* is an endangered national treasure.

"We built a sense of pride around the species," Butler recounted, "and created an understanding about its habitat. We used the parrot to protect the forests. It is hard to talk about forest preservation to poor people, but they can identify with the endangered national bird."

Butler went directly to the school children, aware that "the kids will talk to their parents about saving the colorful national symbol." His German-born wife, Magda, would come along dressed in a colorful parrot costume. Butler, "a happily maniacal cheerleader," according to one account, would lead the children in song, hand out parrot T-shirts, flap his arms in a birdlike fashion, issue parrot badges, and talk about the importance of the endemic bird as the national symbol. The parrot is even found on the St. Lucian passport to remind travelers of the national bird.

Another Butler gimmick is the "Jacquot Express," an exhibition bus brightly painted with a likeness of the parrot and its rainforest surroundings. Through a loudspeaker it squawks, "Save the forest!" Models inside demonstrate the ravages of erosion and the destruction of the forest.

Butler stresses to one and all the importance of the forests to the bird and to all living creatures on the island. "THINK BEFORE YOU CUT OUR TREES: FORESTS FOR LIFE," one billboard proclaims.

Called "promoting protection through pride," the program worked wonders. St. Lucians stopped capturing the bird for pets and sale, and stopped others from doing so as well. Young people forsook their slingshots. The parrot population has jumped from about 100 in the late 1970s to around 250—roughly the carrying capacity of the island—in 1990. Deforestation slowed greatly, although it did not stop completely. The St. Lucian government signed the Convention on International Trade in Endangered Species (CITES), ratified by 112 nations as of early 1992, that governs international trade of threatened animals and plants.

The St. Lucian program was so effective, in fact, that Butler was asked by the RARE Center for Tropical Bird Conservation, a U.S. nonprofit organization, to adapt his program for other Caribbean islands, as species endemic to any one small island habitat are particularly vulnerable to extinction. Sponsored by RARE, Butler took his campaign to Barbados, the Bahamas, the Cayman Islands, Dominica, St. Vincent, and Montserrat.

A new "protection through pride manual," a 150-page environmental "cookbook," as Butler describes it, on how to implement a St. Lucian-style conservation program, has been produced and distributed so that islanders throughout the region can create their own local conservation programs. The cookbook approach allows Butler to transfer his recipes to various islands with a minimum of personal oversight.

Now a St. Lucian national, Butler has frankly abandoned his career as an ornithologist to become a "conservation marketer." He argues, "You wouldn't expect an engineer to sell the car he designs; you shouldn't ask pure scientists to sell conservation to the public—it takes special salesmanship."

Various endangered Caribbean birds now have become a vehicle for advocating forest preservation. On the island nation of St. Vincent, a local brewery adopted "Vincie the Parrot" as the corporate symbol and supports conservationist messages mixed with beer advertisements. "If Parrots were People, They'd Drink Hairoun," a T-shirt claims. A calypso song written by a St. Vincent forester admonishes, "Leave de National Bird in de Wild."

The Imperial Parrot, locally called the "Sisserou," adorns the flag of Dominica, another island neighbor. A Butler-inspired campaign had children donating money to save its forest habitat and an

Bruno P. (for Penguin) Zehnder frolics among penguins he fights to protect from humanity's encroachment into Antarctica. (Photo by Heather May. © 1992 by Bruno P. Zehnder.)

oil company bumper sticker announcing, "West Indies Oil and the Sisserou, Second to None."

In years past, miners took canaries down into mines with them. If the birds became sick, it was a sign that toxic gases were building up and the miners' environment was threatened. Similarly, Paul Butler, supported by the insights of Gabriel Charles, is using brightly colored Caribbean parrots to warn islanders that their habitat is in danger.

Butler's next test will be to design an awareness program for the larger, more diverse Caribbean nations where it is more challenging to mount a conservation campaign. But the driven salesman cannot be underestimated.

Paul Butler and Gabriel Charles are good examples of two laureates who worked through the government to save birds. Jom Malai, on the other hand, a 1990 Global 500 winner in Thailand, is a self-taught environmentalist who fought both the government and his neighbors to protect birds.

A retired farmer who was seventy-five when he won the award, Malai told reporter Normita Thongtham, a 1988 Global 500 laureate (see page 71), that birds began visiting his small farm twenty-five years earler: "At first very few came, then their numbers gradually increased as they realized that this was a safe place."

Malai, also known as Uncle Jom, and his sister-in-law Nok enjoyed the birds and chased away hunters and neighborhood boys with slingshots. Thongtham wrote that he "risked his life chasing away hunters." He became more and more enamoured with cormorants, open-billed storks, and other species that came to his place. Rather than discourage the birds, he removed the scarecrows that protected his rice.

Malai laboriously built a swampy area so marsh-dwelling birds would have a place to breed. He told Thongtham that bird droppings killed the mango trees in his orchard. The birds were taking over his modest land, but he reasoned, "If we don't give them shelter they will have nowhere to go and they will die."

The birds increasingly gathered on the farmer's land to create a natural wonder. As part of an international tourist campaign in 1987, the Thai government, which had been criticized for pushing economic development without heed to the environment, promoted Malai's farm as a tourist site and built an observation tower. Malai's farm has been formally declared a Bird Conservation Unit by the Royal Forestry Department, and the bird sanctuary is now seen as a national asset.

Bruno P. Zehnder is another rare bird. The forty-six-year-old Swiss is just crazy about penguins. He is the "Penguin Man" who, after asking his mother's permission, legally changed his middle initial to "P" to honor his love for penguins.

"My thinking and energy," said the 1987 award winner, "is encircled by penguins." The outgoing, friendly photographer claims they have a therapeutic value. "If you are depressed, just look at a penguin," he told us. "They will make you happy. They are innocent, positive, and humorous birds.

"Penguins are near-sighted and curious. But you shouldn't stand over them; it makes them a little nervous. The best way to approach a penguin is on your stomach. Speak Swiss German to them, they like the 'umlaut' [a soft *u* sound in German]."

Zehnder signs his correspondence, "Guardian of Antarctica," and claims "a youth dream put penguins in the back of [his] mind forever. At a restaurant in New York City, where he has lived since 1979, Zehnder explained to us his long journey to the fulfilling discovery, "I am Antarctica and Antarctica is me."

Born in 1945 in Bad Ragaz, Switzerland, he found his surroundings stifling early on, as "my father's thinking only went to the Swiss border." He yearned to "see what is out there," so, upon finishing military training in 1965, he left Switzerland to wander the world. He "traveled on a shoestring," but not like a hippie, earning money with his linguistic skills.

In 1975 he served as a steward on a Danish icebreaker in Antarctic waters and "immediately fell in love with the continent." For Zehnder it was "a religious experience to find an untouched refuge in this world."

A self-taught photographer, he used his camera "as an instrument to capture this pure world." He sold his pictures in Japan and managed to return to the region to take more shots. The increased fame of his pictures made it easier for Zehnder, who speaks six languages, to travel to Antarctica as an expedition photographer. When we interviewed him in late 1991, he had already visited the region seventeen times, vowing to keep returning "for the rest of my life."

Zehnder's devotion to the icy region is reflected even in his marriage to Heather May, an American actress. The ceremony took place in Antarctica after a long struggle to obtain seats on airplanes, usually reserved only for scientists and their retinue. Her pictures show Zehnder in white tie and tails cavorting with similarly appearing birds. "Penguins," he told us in one of his many cryptic statements, "are the symbol of my life."

Like many single-cause environmentalists, Zehnder is adept at self-advertisement. But his striking photographs also speak directly and effectively for the preservation of Antarctica's five million square miles and all the creatures that depend on its forbidding habitat.

Penguins are near the top of the Antarctic food chain. The birds eat mainly krill, tiny shrimplike crustaceans, which in turn eat algae. Both krill and algae could be damaged by ultraviolet rays coming through the thinning ozone layer above the Antarctic that is being depleted by man-made chemicals. Scientists are monitoring the number and health of Antarctic penguins to gauge the effects of the ozone hole, as well as other forms of environmental disturbance, on the food chain.

The more people are made aware of the penguin, the more they are apt to understand the vulnerability of the bird's environment. No one has done more than Bruno Zehnder to popularize the bird that seems so amusing to humans, but whose life is in fact a grim struggle for survival. Zehnder's photographs are now regularly exhibited in the great museums of the world. They also appear on magazine covers and posters, and one of his penguin pictures even decorates a major credit card. He has deservedly won various august photographic and environmental awards.

In a singular salute to his work, huge blowups of his photographs surrounded the signing of a moratorium on the exploitation of Antarctica's mineral resources. The protocol to the thirty-nine-nation Antarctic Treaty, signed on October 4, 1991, in Madrid's 450-year-old Santa Cruz Palace, has loopholes; but the international agreement was a clear step forward. Zehnder likes to think that his photographs lent a "penguin mood" of good will and optimism to the proceedings. If nothing else, they reminded delegates of their obligation to preserve the continent's fragile beauty and wildlife.

"Scientists say that you shouldn't call penguins 'cute,'" Zehnder told us, "but I do. My job is to get people to identify with them." In much the same way that Paul Butler perceives that songs and billboards about the Caribbean parrot are a vehicle for tropical forest preservation, Zehnder understands that photographs of the penguin serve as an instrument for preserving Antarctica's wintry ecosystem.

3

The Rhino Man

The huge and hostile rhinoceros has become an icon of the world's vanishing wildlife. On one hand, the behemoth symbolizes the plight of an animal whose life-sustaining habitat is being taken over by man. Some rhinos grow to two meters tall and weigh as much as 2,200 kilograms. Like elephants, they need extensive grazing territory. Human populations in Africa and Asia are rapidly growing, forcing land-hungry farmers to invade the rhino's traditional terrain, where humans and beast cannot hope to coexist.

On the other hand, the so-called "mobile pharmacy" is vulnerable to man's ignorant pursuit of its horn and other body parts for folk medicine. Africans, Arabs, Chinese, Europeans, and Indians have pursued the rhino's horn for more than 1,000 years, believing it will provide them with a cure-all medicine, a good-luck charm, a handsome adornment, a status-giving knife handle, or an aphrodisiac. The horn can weigh as much as five-and-half kilograms and sell for as much as $28,000 a kilogram in Yemen and in East Asian nations.

The rhino, however, is not without defenders. Kenyan Global 500 laureate Michael Werikhe, for instance, has become known as the "Rhino Man" for his advocacy of one of the animal kingdom's ugliest beasts, at least to human eyes.

There were an estimated 70,000 rhinos worldwide at the start of the 1970s; at the end of the 1980s there were about 11,500. All five species—two African and three Asian—are endangered. In Kenya alone, an estimated 98 percent of all the nation's rhinos have been killed off in less than twenty years.

The two African species—the black and the white rhino—have misleading names. In fact, both are grey in color and are differentiated by the shape of their lips. What they share is possible extinction. "Three tons of muscle, two inches of armor, one hundred pounds of weaponry," proclaims a conservationist slogan, "and it's completely defenseless" against habitat destruction and poachers with modern arms.

Since he was a small boy, Michael Werikhe loved animals, especially snakes. He first became aware of the rhino's plight when he took a menial post in his country's wildlife service. His first job was in the Ivory Room, sorting rhino horns and elephant tusks for government auction. There he became "very disturbed" by the constant inflow of horns and tusks caused by the poacher's gun.

"The animals, I knew, didn't die of natural causes," he recounted. "Poaching was out of control. Very disillusioned, I left." In 1977, it should be noted, the Kenyan government finally outlawed tusk and horn auctions.

Werikhe, a poor, minimally educated young man with limited career prospects, would hardly have seemed to be in a position to quit the economic security of a government job. Working for the wildlife service could have been the first step toward his lifelong dream of becoming a game warden.

The serious-minded young man next found work in his home town of Mombasa, a vibrant seaport on the Indian Ocean, as a security guard at the Associated Vehicle Assemblers Limited (AVA) plant. He was still greatly disturbed, however, about the plight of the rhino. He learned that various activists around the world had brought attention to their particular concern by the simple act of walking. If they could do it, he thought, so could he.

Other environmentalists who walk to publicize and raise funds for a given environmental issue are found on the Global 500 Roll of

Conservationist Michael Werikhe is pictured with an orphaned baby black rhino. Werikhe visited some 30 cities during his five-month North American tour called the Rhino Walk. Although he was not accompanied by a rhino, Werikhe was joined by supporters at zoos and aquariums on the tour. (Photograph © by Duncan Willets, Camerapix)

Honor. Robert Swan, a young energetic British environmentalist, for example, walked to both the North and the South poles to plant a United Nations flag. Finally, he marched down the main aisle of the United Nations General Assembly to present the flag to then Secretary General Javier Perez de Cuellar. After making his point about defending polar environments, he went on to a career of preaching environmentalism to young people and organizing youth groups, winning the Global 500 in 1989.

Riel Huaorani, a Canadian Indian medical student and a 1990 laureate, walks to rally young people for regional reforestation projects. Dressed in full tribal regalia, with braided hair, the Iridamant-Micmac Indian has taken a "re-greening the planet" message by foot to the youth of Africa, the Mediterranean, and North America. In 1989, Huaorani was elected International President of Young People's Planet, a pluralistic youth movement, and moved to Italy.

Werikhe, who had neither Huaorani's exotic regalia nor Swan's dramatic destinations, planned his first walk carefully. On applications he designed himself, he solicited sponsors for a trek from Mombasa to Nairobi, the capital of Kenya. Married, with two daughters, he worked extra hours to earn complimentary time off from AVA for the trip.

He made the 480-kilometer trip in 1982 to publicize the killing of the black rhino, an animal he had never seen. As a conversation piece he draped two snakes over his shoulders. Along the way, he solicited the roadside views of his countrymen on the importance of Kenya's endangered rhinos.The walk was a success, raising consciousness and money on behalf of the endangered megaherbivore, whose closest living relatives, surprisingly, are the horse and the tapir.

In 1985, he walked across Kenya, Tanzania, and Uganda, again carrying on a dialogue with his fellow Africans. He asked: "Is the rhino worth saving? If so, how do we do it?" At first the people seemed apathetic. But once he explained the animal's predicament, he found widespread concern and willingness to help. He came away with this philosophy: "Give Africans good information, then they will do something."

During the trans-African tour, Werikhe also discovered that he really did not like walking, especially in the rain. The trek demanded that he carry on his back everything he might need—a weighty pile that put severe stress on his back and legs. But he carried on. In 1988, he walked 2,800 kilometers from Italy to England by way of Switzerland, Germany, and Holland, and in 1991 he spent five months walking across North America.

By the end of 1991, the thirty-five-year-old African had walked thousands of kilometers, a painful challenge at times, on behalf of an animal he certainly does not anthropomorphize. Although he had raised more than $2 million for rhino-protection projects, he did not profit personally.

Why does he do it? As his employer, P.J.C. Hughes put it, "He is no romantic nut case. In his life, as in his walking, his feet are always planted firmly upon the ground." Obviously Werikhe's rhino walks bring him recognition. He has met presidents and princes and has heard the applause of the crowd. But he seems largely untouched by his celebrity.

When a walk is over, he goes back to his job at AVA. Hughes points out, "The company has granted him some sabbatical time for his rhino projects, but not much and not often. For most of his walks and tours, he has used his own earned leave days."

We caught up with Werikhe in 1991 in Washington, D.C., during his North American "Rhino Walk" sponsored by the American Association of Zoological Parks and Aquariums (AAZPA). Werikhe had a full schedule. A series of events—celebrity appearances, speaking engagements, dinners, and walks—had been arranged by AAZPA and The Discovery Channel, which updated his progress across the country on cable television. At these and other events, he sought funds for rhino survival projects. Three-quarters of the money he raised was earmarked for African rhino programs and the rest for AAZPA's species survival project.

Concluding his thirty-city trip in Washington, the soft-spoken, bespectacled African said, "Walking has allowed me to learn about the environment, especially at the people's level. You don't need to be a trained conservationist, you don't need a degree to improve the world. I got my degrees in the bush. Just open the door of your house—look at the animals, birds, trees and ask yourself, 'What can I do to protect the environment?' "

Clearly a very intelligent and observant man, he is far more than a pitchman to publicize the plight of the rhino. He has a message both for Westerners and Africans. For his own people, he says, "The rhino is a living symbol of our environment. It is a big animal, easy to watch. If something is happening to this big animal, just imagine the problems of small animals and our total environment."

As for Western environmentalists, he notes, "No matter how much money you put into a rhino-protection program, if it doesn't have the support of the people, it is doomed to fail."

Werikhe hopes to walk across Taiwan and other heavy horn-consuming nations to deliver a third message: The purchase of "magic medicine" has no scientific basis and is leading to the extinction of an animal that has walked the earth largely unvexed for thirty million years.

In addition to a walker like Michael Werikhe, it will take informed and convincing African environmentalists in leadership positions to save vulnerable animals. Increasingly throughout the Third World, effective individuals and institutions are emerging to defend the local environment. A 1988 Global 500 winner from Kenya, Perez Malande Olindo, epitomizes the new breed of trained Third World environmentalists.

We met Olindo, an unpretentious and friendly man, at the offices of an international wildlife organization in downtown Nairobi. After studying wildlife management in the United States, he said he "made wildlife his profession, his religion, his way of life." He pointed out that traditionally, Africans "revered certain trees, birds, and animals as holding a spiritual value. Scientific explanations of their value came long after the religious significance was perceived."

Olindo, a former director of Kenya's Wildlife Conservation and Management Department, is convinced, like most African environmentalists, that the average citizen is the key to the country's ecological future. "Elephants don't vote, people do," he said, "and the concerns of the elephant are not heard. But in a land where tourism is based on wildlife, if the wildlife disappears, so will the income from tourism. Animals are the best workers in the country and they don't get paid. They don't go on strike, they don't go on leave, and they live on marginal land that can't be properly used for agriculture."

Olindo took his message to areas where people competed with wildlife for land. "We worked toward harmony," he said. "Now many more people see the animals as a national asset, not a liability."

Can Myths Kill?

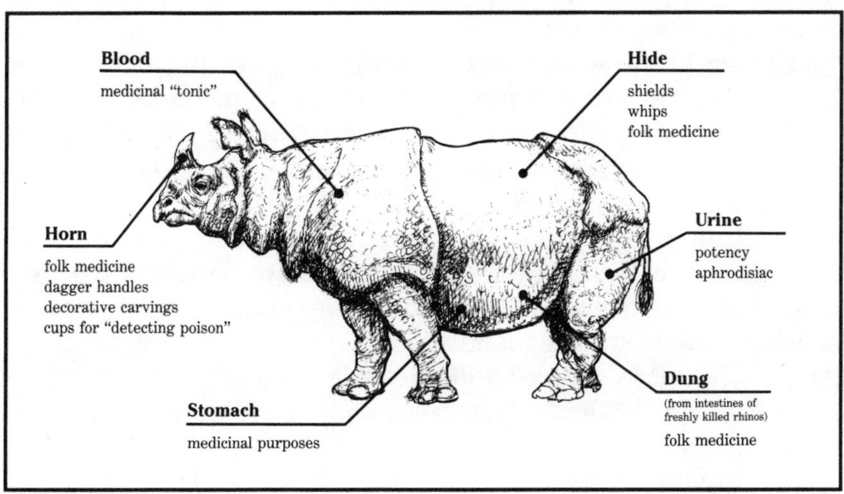

Yes, myths can kill. In some parts of the world, people think that products made from a rhino's body have special properties. They associate the rhino's strength with an ability to cure disease and to give strength or sexual potency.

Rhino products, especially those made from horn, bring high prices—more than $60,000 for one rhino horn.

As a result we are destroying the world's rhinos. In 1970, about 70,000 rhinos were alive; in 1989, only about 11,500 rhinos lived in the wild.

(Illustration and caption information courtesy of the National Zoo, Washington, DC)

But in a country where the per capita annual income is less than $400 and rhino and elephant tusks can fetch thousands of dollars, Olindo well understood that Kenya had to get tough with poachers. At the beginning of a ten-year stint as the director of the park service in 1966, he estimated that Kenya had a black rhino population of nearly 20,000. When he returned to the park service in 1987, there were fewer than 600 left.

During his absence, illegal hunting had gone unchecked. The activities of dangerous gunmen roaming the game parks so threatened the tourist business that President Daniel arap Moi's regime could no longer ignore the issue. Olindo was brought back to solve the embarrassing problem.

In addition to traditional Kenyan poachers, Somalians displaced by civil war and drought were drifting across the border and beginning to participate in the illicit trade in large numbers. The foreign poachers, often trained soldiers, had arms and knew how to use them. Park officials were outgunned. Kenya instituted a shoot-to-kill policy, which Olindo defended, pointing out laconically, "They shoot to kill us."

The organized poachers were finally reined in. The presence of the Somalian poachers was politically helpful. Instead of seeming to battle on behalf of rich foreign tourists against poor Kenyans who were trying to make money as best they could, the government's anti-poacher campaign was said to repel the Somalian invaders. Olindo knows, however, that "in the long run the people must share and understand the benefits of wildlife preservation, or we will fail."

The difficulty and expense involved in trying to protect a huge wild animal fiercely pursued by poachers is stunning. To show what it took to maintain rhinos in Kenya, Olindo sent us to Nakuru National Park's rhino sanctuary. At the park, a cadre of eleven armed rhino guards, a twenty-three man maintenance crew, and three technicians were constantly on alert to oversee a handful of rhinos. The endangered animals were kept behind electrified fences in a setting that was halfway between the rhino's natural environment and a zoo.

With a system akin to a military operation, the headquarters has a wall with color-coded pins to show where their ear-tagged wards were last spotted. Each rhino has a name like Helen, Rhoda, Rodney, and Winnie, and a guard to verify its good health and where-

Anna Merz, the "Rhino Woman," was selected in 1990 for the Global 500 Roll of Honor because of her efforts to save rhinos on her Kenyan ranch. (Copyright © by Camerapix, Nairobi, Kenya)

abouts daily. "We can take nothing for granted," said James Mulwa, the park's chief of rhino surveillance.

Anna Merz, a 1990 laureate, earned the nickname "Rhino Woman" for her personal effort to save the ponderous animal on her Kenyan ranch. Her award citation notes that she "invested her entire savings, time, and energy into the project. Despite many difficulties—including drought and poachers—there are now five white rhinos and thirteen black rhinos in the sanctuary."

It will take the combined talents of the walker Michael Werikhe, the wildlife manager Perez Olindo, the frontlines guardian Anna Merz, and many more like them to save the rhino from exctinction. Otherwise, the once unchallenged wild animal will stay a rare and expensively kept relic.

4

Tree Huggers

Trees stand as palpable symbols of the environmental movement. They provide a crucial—and highly visible—link in the Earth's ecosystem. Deforestation has different results in different regions of the world, but there is one common feature: ecological disaster. From landslides careening down the mountain slopes of Nepal, to the silting of rivers in Thailand, from the destruction of wildlife habitat in Kenya, to the extinction of medicinally useful plants in Brazil, the results of deforestation—except for short-term economic development—are never positive.

> *Come, arise, my brothers and sisters,*
> *Save this mountain . . .*
> *Come plant new trees, new forests*
> *Decorate the earth.*
>
> ***—Chipko Andolan song***

Among people aware of these frightening consequences, there is an instinctual urge to protect the "grandes dames" of nature by encircling them with their arms, as a parent would a child. This notion has given rise to the pejorative term "tree huggers," used by many opponents of environmental conservation to denigrate activists.

However, a group in India cofounded by Global 500 laureate Chandi Prasad Bhatt is using this action to further its goals, with great success. The group calls itself the *Chipko Andolan,* or "movement to hug the trees."

In the Himalayan region of Gopeshwar, where the *Chipko* movement originated, the people depend heavily on the surrounding forest for fuelwood and fodder. Bhatt was born in this rural area in 1932 to a poor peasant family. He was one of few villagers in his area to earn a high school diploma. He began teaching but quit after a short time because the salary was too low and irregular, opting instead for a job as a booking clerk for the local bus company. The job brought him into contact with pilgrims traveling to local temples. Among the crowds were many workers in the *sarvodaya* (welfare for all) movement inspired by Mahatma Gandhi's urging "to work for the uplift of Indian society, beginning in the lowly village."

Inspired by Gandhi's ideals, Bhatt used his leave time to visit villages where *sarvodaya* workers were holding meetings and starting self-help projects. In 1959, he participated in a fifteen-day march through the region. During this time of tension between India and China, the movement was guided by the philosophy that India's best defense lay in its rural people. So Bhatt quit his job at the bus company to devote all his energies to bettering the life of his fellow villagers.

Because Gopeshwar lies near the border of Chinese-occupied Tibet, the Indian government began building a network of roads there for defense, bringing in great numbers of soldiers as well as skilled laborers from India's plains region. Along with the influx of people came massive deforestation. Burgeoning populations required more and more fuelwood, and new roads that opened the frontier to the military also opened previously inaccessible forests to commercial use. The government, which owned most of the forest, gave logging rights to commercial companies from the plains, excluding the local people from economic gains.

The loss of tree cover, which had served to anchor the soil on the steep mountainsides, had disastrous consequences. Bhatt discovered this during trips he took through his home district to spread the *sarvodaya* ideals. Traveling by bus through the mountains, he learned that a landslide had swept another bus off the road into a deep gorge, killing twenty-four of the passengers. A week later, he heard heavy rains had triggered another landslide that covered an entire village. Only one child survived. These events brought Bhatt face-to-face with the environmental destruction aggravated by recent development.

To help the villagers reap more benefits from the changes, in 1964 he founded the Dasholi Gram Swarajya Mandal (DGSM)—the Dasholi Society for Village Self-Rule. Its goal was to establish small forest-product industries that would provide better-paid, permanent employment for local villagers.

The DGSM set up a carpentry shop and sought contracts to cut trees to make tools, but government-connected commercial lumbermen were able to outbid the villagers. To cut out greedy middlemen, the DGSM next tried to market directly to villagers medicinal herbs they bought from gatherers. The DGSM and seven other village cooperatives also set up small factories to produce turpentine from tree sap. However, the villagers had trouble acquiring an adequate allocation of sap. They had to pay more for the raw material than the large factory in the plains, which got its supply at a government-subsidized rate.

In 1971, villagers protested the two-tiered pricing system and made demands on the government. When there was no response, Bhatt decided to speak for the people. He traveled for a year to garner support for the villagers' demands, drawing some media attention to the issue. After more fruitless demonstrations, the DGSM began to seek more effective means of protest.

In the meantime, a further complaint had arisen. The DGSM carpentry shop was denied its annual quota of ash trees for the production of farming tools; the government gave the rights instead to a large manufacturer of sporting goods.

When the company's loggers came to Gopeshwar, the DGSM had to find a nonviolent way to stop them. Bhatt, adopting a tactic used by village women back in the 1700s, suggested the villagers go into the woods and embrace the trees, challenging the woodcutters to swing their axes against the unarmed villagers' backs. And so the tree hugger movement was born.

Each time the villagers of an area learned their forests were being marked for felling, they swarmed into the forest to confront the lumbermen and company agents. The lumbermen would turn away, only to come back later. The government began to offer concessions to the DGSM to stop the demonstrations, but the group held out for full satisfaction of its demands:

- a complete review of forest policy to ensure the hill people's natural rights to their share of forest wealth,
- priority to local cottage industries in the allocation of forest wealth, and
- a voice in forest management and administration by the local populations.

Finally, the government formed a study panel of geologists, forest officials, irrigation experts, and representatives of the *Chipko* movement. The panel's final report recommended a halt to all tree felling for ten years and regulations against overgrazing of cattle and building of fires. It also suggested that areas below 3,000 meters be reforested and suitable varieties of grasses be planted above the tree line. The government accepted the report's recommendations in April 1977, banning all tree felling in a 1,200-square-kilometer area for ten years. Similar bans were enacted in other regions.

Following on this success, the DGSM, under Bhatt's guidance, began organizing a series of Environment Conservation Camps where villagers, students, scientists, and forestry officials lived together for five days. They built retaining walls, dug holes for tree seedlings, and weeded and fertilized planted saplings. They also discussed environmental and agricultural topics and village problems—exchanges that often led to government action.

Planting carried out by the villagers proved highly successful, with a survival rate of 68–88 percent, compared to only 15–56 percent for trees planted under government reforestation programs.

For his role in the *Chipko* movement, Bhatt won the Raymond Magsaysay Award for Community Leadership in 1982. Not surprisingly, he gave the $20,000 prize money to the DGSM. Though still active in the organization, Bhatt's sphere of influence has widened considerably with the *Chipko* movement's growing success. He serves on government environmental commissions, is often consulted by Indian forest experts and government officials, and has spoken at international conferences.

At a 1981 United Nations-sponsored conference on renewable sources of energy, Bhatt told the delegates that "forest dwellers cannot be prohibited by law from satisfying their basic needs from the forests . . . Unless we find a framework in which forests and people can live together, one or the other will be destroyed. Saving the trees is only the first step. Saving ourselves is the real goal."

Bhatt's original concern with the economic welfare of his fellow villagers eventually led him to focus on environmental concerns, specifically the protection of trees. Michael Odula, on the other hand, began his work with trees as his focus.

Odula is headmaster of the Tom Mboya secondary school on the small Kenyan island of Rusinga in Lake Victoria, literally a stone's

Michael Odula examines seedlings that will eventually be planted in his native Kenya as part of his reforestation efforts. (Photograph by Elizabeth Lee)

throw from the mainland. The institution, which he founded in the mid-1970s, now enrolls 400 boys from the ages of fifteen to nineteen.

We had met Odula in Mexico City when he came to accept his Global 500 award, and he invited us to visit his school. In Nairobi on other business, we decided to accept his invitation. However, we could not warn him because there is no telephone on the island. So suddenly, five months later, we arrived with no announcement.

"Since I came back," he told us, "I became a very important person in this country." We sat on a couch in the dusty heat of his small office, sharing the room with an egg-laying hen. Odula proudly showed us clippings from the Kenyan press on his tree-planting and soil conservation work. He then showed us around the island to inspect his projects.

Odula was born on Rusinga Island and used to walk the woods with his grandfather. "When I was a little boy," he said, pointing to a barren mound in the distance, "this hilltop was covered with trees—tall trees, indigenous trees. Now it is only shrubs." People began to cut trees to provide firewood, build houses, and clear land for cultivation. But a rapidly growing population soon caused the cutting to get out of hand. In 1963, the 115-square-kilometer island held only 9,000 people. By 1990, with an annual growth rate of 3.8 percent, there were 22,000.

The island people survive by subsistence agriculture and fishing. Odula noticed as he grew older that crops were harder and harder to cultivate, as the loss of trees had led to less rainfall and the erosion of fertile soil. Also, with fewer trees around, women had to walk farther onto the mainland to gather firewood.

In 1980, Odula put into action a plan to reverse the destruction of his homeland. With his students' help, he grew seedlings on the school grounds that he then gave for free to fellow islanders to raise awareness about the problem. He held public meetings with local chiefs "to try to explain the importance of planting trees." He then began selling the seedlings —100 for ten Kenyan shillings—to make people realize their value.

Buyers were taught how to plant, water, and prune their young trees and protect them from hungry livestock. In the tradition of agroforestry, Odula offered nitrogen-fixing trees to help fertilize the soil. He also cultivated trees specifically for firewood, building, ornamentation, and medicine.

But soon after the tree-planting effort took root, Odula realized that reforestation alone was not going to solve Rusinga Island's problems. "Trees don't grow overnight," he pointed out as we walked, and they were still being cut as fast as they grew. As if to underscore his point, a pair of young girls trudged by on the dusty road that rings the island, each bearing a large bundle of firewood on her head.

So Odula added a program of energy conservation based on the use of more energy-efficient clay cookstoves. The new model requires much less wood than the traditional open-fire stove, which wastes 60 percent of the energy generated. As an impetus to villagers reluctant to give up the familiar open-flame cooking method, he has installed in his school an institution-size clay stove that has cut wood consumption from ten truckloads per term to three truckloads.

He has branched out in other ways, too. A windmill he installed now pumps water up from the freshwater lake to irrigate crops and trees. He is looking into the possibility of harnessing solar energy. And he has begun work on a terracing system to shore up an eroding hillside that archaeologist Louis Leakey stripped bare in his efforts to excavate prehistoric human fossils.

Odula has spread his conservation campaign to other schools, churches, and women's groups in the area, giving workshops on agroforestry and energy conservation. He has also introduced traditional methods of agriculture into the curriculum of his school. Before, he said, "agriculture was just for someone who failed their academic courses." Odula teaches that agriculture is a valuable skill permitting self-reliance in the face of high national unemployment. "It is difficult for people to change," he remarked. "It takes time." That is why he likes to teach the students when they are young, so that "they grow with that conservation attitude."

The tree-planting program was far more successful than he imagined, and trees from the school's nursery can now be seen as far as twenty kilometers away on the mainland. "When I walk around the island I'm very proud," Odula told us, as he can see the many trees that have come from his nursery. Already he has noticed an increase in rainfall on the island. There are also trees for shade from the searing sun. Now island people "talk about trees, about the importance of trees," he boasted. "Isn't that something great?"

But Odula is not completely content. "We lacked exposure" to information and ideas before his winning of the Global 500 in 1987, he said. During our visit he spoke grandly of his hope to build an international environmental study center on Rusinga Island. He was also nominated to head a new chapter of the Children's Alliance for the Protection of the Environment (CAPE), a 1990 Global 500 winner, planned for Rusinga Island.

Odula's vision has been expanding ever since he started his first nursery back in 1980. In 1986, he traveled to Scandinavia for a three-month forestry course on a fellowship from the Danish Development Association (DANIDA). It was his first trip outside of Kenya. The Global 500 award brought him to Mexico City, and the following year UNESCO sponsored his attendance at a teachers' exchange program in Finland to study international education.

Each experience has led to a new insight on ecological interrelationships; each trip abroad has taught him that problems are shared. "We are one family," he says of the planet. "We share problems, but we also share solutions."

Kenya is also the scene of another inspiring reforestation effort. The Green Belt Movement is responsible for the planting of more than ten million trees across the landscape of the East African nation since its founding in 1977. Some 80 percent of the trees—which come from the movement's 600-odd nurseries—have matured. About 50,000 women have participated, cultivating a more positive self-image in a culture that by tradition discounts women's contributions to society. Over one million children have also been involved, learning a lesson about environmental protection that they will carry with them into adulthood.

The movement has blossomed under the charismatic leadership of Wangari Maathai, an outspoken woman whose birth into Kenya's elite gave her the opportunity in the 1960s to study biology in the United States at the Academy of Mount St. Scholastica and the University of Pittsburgh. She returned to Kenya, earning a Ph.D. at the University of Nairobi and becoming the first female Ph.D. instructor there.

In her youth, Maathai had been taught by her elders that children bore special responsiblities for the development of the newly emerging nation. At the age of twenty-five, having secured her university position, she began to fulfill that role.

Her first effort was a cleanup program in the Nairobi neighborhood of Langata in which landlords would pay jobless people to plant trees, trim hedges, tend lawns, sweep streets, and cut grass. The project withered for lack of funding and public awareness, but it did direct Maathai to the 1976 Habitat conference (United Nations Conference on Human Settlement) in Vancouver, Canada.

Upon her return, she was invited to speak about the conference at the Annual General Meeting of the National Council of Women of Kenya (NCWK). That address from the poised and eloquent educator brought her an appointment to the Executive Committee of the NCWK, and she joined its Standing Committee on Environment and Habitat. The committee was seeking a project to support, and Maathai suggested a community tree-planting effort, to be called "Save the Land Harambee," *harambee* meaning "let's all pull together."

The project's first tree-planting ceremony was held in Nairobi on World Environment Day, June 5, 1977. Seven trees were planted, in honor of two women and five men, all deceased, who had made significant contributions to their communities. But the city council, which was to care for the trees, did not follow through. By 1992, only two trees survived.

Fortunately, the follow-up activities were much more successful. The group organized a tree-planting event in Naivasha, timed to coincide with the United Nations Conference on Desertification, to highlight how rural people suffer from desertification. With the financial support of Mobil Oil of Kenya, they planted a swath of trees on land owned by a cooperative of 800 rural women. They also launched a national campaign—using radio, television, newspapers, magazines, church meetings, workshops, and seminars—to inform the public about desertification and how to combat the process.

Following these efforts, the NCWK office began to receive requests from all over Kenya to plant trees and donate seedlings. So the group obtained seeds—free at first, then later for a nominal charge—as well as technical and moral support from the Department of Forestry.

The NCWK soon recognized the need to plant large tree plots on public land as examples of community reforestation. Many of the plots were planted on public school compounds. Trees were planted around the boundaries to encircle the schoolgrounds with "belts" of green. Thus the name Green Belt evolved.

At the public plantings, crowds would scramble for free NCWK seedlings. To satisfy the demand, the NCWK set up its own nursery. And so the Green Belt Movement found its format.

With the movement's success, Maathai has been catapulted into the international development arena. She is invited to speak at conferences, quoted in news articles, and cited in references to grassroots success. At the Global Assembly of Women and the Environment, held in Miami, Florida, in November 1991, we were able to hear her explain the movement to a small workshop of participants.

"It is," she said, "the answer to the question that keeps coming up all the time: what can we do?" Its manifold aims are to provide fuelwood, stop soil erosion, improve nutrition, save endangered indigenous plants and trees, generate income for women and thus improve their standing, and raise public awareness of environment and development issues.

"I had this idea," Maathai recalled, "that perhaps we could plant trees to solve all these problems. Fortunately in this area you don't need much technology or much money. You don't need money to dig a hole. But you do need a lot of commitment."

And the commitment has been forthcoming from tens of thousands of Kenyans—most of them women. Traditionally, African women are expected to work for nothing, Maathai said bluntly, but "show me one forester who is doing anything free of charge." The movement pays a small sum, about twenty-five cents, to women for each tree they plant. The money is paid only when it has survived at least three months outside the nursery, and district monitors check all claims.

The whole process has been helpful in raising the esteem of the women involved, not only in their own eyes but also in the eyes of the community. "If you feel very angry," Maathai advised, "dig a hole. And when the tree starts growing, you feel very good." Trees grow very fast in much of Kenya, she added, with some species maturing within five years. "When people see the trees growing," she explained, "they look at women differently. They see the women doing something positive."

The process, which emphasizes reliance on self rather than on government foresters, helps people "to know themselves," to understand themselves, to speak for themselves. This message has helped the movement spread to twenty-five of Kenya's forty-five districts. In some districts it has been especially successful because a good climate and fertile soil have brought quick growth and visible success.

In some areas, however, the people are illiterate or speak only a local dialect, complicating information dissemination. Written materials must be translated into the local language, and community trainers hired. In more arid districts, the lack of water allows for only hundreds, not thousands, of trees. Success is possible there, Maathai said, "but that requires the kind of money we don't have."

"We've been working with peanuts," she complained, but by 1992 the movement operated on a $500,000 budget supported by the United Nations, the African Development Foundation, and various American and Scandinavian nongovernmental organizations. The movement's secretariat in Nairobi, with a staff of thirty, is equipped with a computer acquired with the help of a new offshoot of the local movement—the Green Belt International Movement.

Part of the reason for the movement's high international profile is Maathai's vocal opposition to a sixty-story office tower that Kenyan President Daniel arap Moi planned to build in Uhuru Park, a large public green space in downtown Nairobi. Maathai and her fellow Green Belters filed a lawsuit against Kenya's governing party, which barely tolerates dissent in this one-party nation. The movement waged a press campaign that helped garner widespread support.

The movement based its opposition, Maathai said, on three points: the developers "were not able to produce an environmental impact report; they had not sought public opinion, even though Uhuru was a public park; and they were going to borrow a huge sum even though the country has great debt already." The building was to cost $200 million, with $150 million to be borrowed from foreign lenders.

The government claimed the building would provide employment as well as a platform for Kenya's first twenty-four-hour television channel. Maathai countered that "buildings don't make employment, not in the long run. And the fact is, only 1 percent of the people own television sets. We need water, food, and medical supplies, not a twenty-four-hour television channel. But this is the ruling party's conception of progress."

In January 1991, Moi announced that the building would be modified to a thirty-story tower. Construction was stymied, however. Maathai said the foreign investors "could see the people didn't want the building and backed off." The campaign against the building was successful, but the movement's fight cost it a great deal of autonomy. "Before," said Maathai, "we were just a bunch of women quietly planting trees. For a long time, nobody knew or even bothered to know what we were doing. Then we stood up not to protect our own rights, our own interests, but the interests of the people. People were amazed to see a bunch of women stand up to the government. It was very empowering not only to women but to other activists."

With such an electric reaction, the Green Belters suddenly found themselves caught up in "environmental advocacy and women's rights," Maathai said. "We find ourselves right in the middle of the fight for human rights. Now we have been called subversive. We have been called underground. We've been called all kinds of things. But we were definitely very overground."

The movement has acquired enemies in Kenya. When it was booted out of its downtown office space, Maathai began to fear for her life. While she believes the group's 1987 Global 500 award "protects us; it strengthens our mandate," it does not protect Maathai herself. She was arrested and briefly jailed in January 1992 for her participation in the Forum for the Restoration of Democracy, the major party opposing Moi's presidency, which he has held since 1978.

Ironically, Moi is a Global 500 laureate, too. We asked Maathai how she felt about his sharing the award. Typically, she is making the best of a strange situation. "In all the letters I write to him, I say, 'You know, you're an environmentalist too; how can you go against us?' "

So the Green Belt Movement labors on. "It's only a drop in the ocean," said Maathai. "What needs to be done on that continent is unimaginable. We can't give up, so we must go on."

Much of the concern about deforestation focuses on the Third World, but many developed countries have already severely depleted their forest resources. In Germany, an industrialized country with advanced deforestation, 1988 Global 500 laureate Karl Partsch is struggling to save Europe's famous mountain range—the Alps—from ruin.

For those who have not seen them, the Alps hold images of pristine snowy peaks broken up by sparsely populated verdant valleys. In fact, the majestic mountains, which stretch from Austria, Bavaria, and Switzerland to northern Italy and southeastern France, are home to some twelve million people. They are also blanketed by highly developed resort towns linked by a network of railways and roads.

Trees have had to make way for development. Those that remain become sick from air pollution and suffer root poisoning. In the Alps, about 80 percent of the air pollution comes from motor vehicle exhaust, a particular problem in mountainous areas because cars emit much more nitric oxide when climbing uphill than on level roads. The rest comes from long-distance industrial pollution.

Tourism, especially the lucrative ski business, bears the brunt of the blame. The Alps contain some 40,000 ski courses, with 119,000 kilometers of slopes and about 14,000 ski lifts. Roads, parking lots, and hotels have sprung up to service the growing industry as well as the summer tourism trade. Seventy percent of the people who live in the Alps depend directly or indirectly on tourism for their livelihood, benefitting from the 100 million people who visit the region every year. The heavy equipment used to develop and maintain facilities is very damaging to seedlings and soil, as is the passage of skiers and hikers over the mountain terrain. And the more tourists who come, the more automobiles they bring in, polluting the Alps even further.

Destruction has been not only visually disturbing, it is life-threatening as well. A serious landslide in the German Alps in 1987 killed more than 100 people, left several hundred injured or homeless, and destroyed millions of dollars of property. "This is a perfect example of what happens when man destroys mountain vegetation," Partsch said. "Eventually the mountains will destroy man."

"I grew up loving nature," said Partsch, who was born in 1922. In college he studied botany and biology. Then, inspired by his famous geographer grandfather, who wrote scientific papers about the Alps and their glaciers, he moved to Germany's Bavarian region. He began designing private and public parks and started a gardening business, developing crossbreeds and new strains of plants and flowers.

One summer day in 1975, local developers began converting forty-five hectares of pastureland near his town into a large golf course. "That day," he explained, "I resolved to fight against such intrusion."

He learned all he could about the dangers facing the Alpine ecosystem. Along with pollution and tourism, he found that livestock and game animals were threatening the mountains. To produce more milk and meat, native cows had been crossbred with American species, creating cattle with smaller, sharper hooves that poked holes in the ground; the holes fill with water and cause erosion. Game animals were eating young trees and shrubs in the highlands because growing urban areas had pushed them out of their natural winter feeding grounds.

Partsch attacked the problems by issuing press statements and talking with officials, demanding a halt to the expansion of ski areas, closer supervision of cattle, and an enforced quota of game hunting. He also began recultivating pastures and woodlands, trying to restore some of the soil-fixing tree cover. On one mountain eroded by skiing and road construction, he organized a planting effort carried out by a youth group and other volunteers. Participants collected seeds of indigenous plants, nurtured them in lowland nurseries, and planted them in erosion-prone areas on the 2,000-meter peak.

Instead of planting young trees, Partsch tries to create a "preforest" environment with small trees and fast-growing shrubs. "We imitate nature," he explained.

He also teaches the concepts of nature to the German public. Partsch has traveled widely to give lectures and hold seminars. His weathered face is also seen on television. Now a member of the European Parliament, Partsch published in 1991 an eighty-page report, complete with cartoons, charts, and graphs, cataloging the various threats to the Alps' ecosystem. Out of his personal parliamentary allowance, he paid for the report's printing and translation into English, French, and Italian. The report's conclusions were unanimously accepted by the Committee on the Environment, Public Health and Consumer Protection.

The report includes a poem, by Harald Grill, which mocks an unfortunately widespread attitude. Translated into English, it reads:

The holiday-makers don't care for the area;
if it is destroyed and devastated,
they will simply go elsewhere for holiday.

The local people don't care for the area either;
if they use it all up, they will go on holiday!

But Partsch, realizing the Alpine region's economic dependence on tourism, does not advocate halting development altogether. Instead he urges tourism development that does not sacrifice the region's natural resources for short-term economic gain, but leaves something for following generations to enjoy.

And he contends much of the destruction is due simply to ignorance. "It is important to teach people about the environment," he said. "Many no longer know how a healthy tree looks and thus cannot recognize the decline."

Partsch believes the Alps offer a good study ground for threatened areas around the world. "The Alps can be likened to an ecological and environmental magnifying glass: a small region where changes that take place all over the Earth are happening more quickly and with rather immediate results."

In the United States 85 percent of the land's primary old-growth forest cover has already been destroyed, but other visionary people are trying to bring some of it back, both for visual beauty and spiritual health.

Andy and Katie Lipkis, a husband-and-wife team of environmental activists living in Beverly Hills, California, spearheaded a community tree-planting effort called TreePeople. Although the 1988 laureates have planted trees in the San Bernadino National Forest and some of California's mountain ranges, their main focus now is urban areas.

"Our emphasis is cities," Katie Lipkis explains, "because we think that's where most of the people are, and if we're going to enroll people in healing the environment, then we're going to have to do it where the people are. And the fact is a city tree can work a lot harder on the environment . . . especially the inner cities. It's an area that most of the major environmental organizations have missed."

Andy and Katie Lipkis

The couple's efforts have gained media attention from coast to coast, focused largely on their book on community action called *The Simple Act of Planting a Tree: A Citizen Forester's Guide to Healing Your Neighborhood, Your City, and Your World*. The book—printed, of course, on recycled paper—encourages readers to plant and nurture trees, and includes a detailed guide to setting up one's own neighborhood tree-planting program based on the TreePeople Citizen Forester program.

The guide walks people through the process of greening a neighborhood, from the intial meeting with a city inspector and organizing the neighbors to recruiting TreePeople volunteers, buying trees, and sending watering instructions to residents.

TreePeople encourages citizens to plant trees for many concrete reasons: they beautify neighborhoods, absorb carbon dioxide, prevent erosion, and offer shade that can help cut air-conditioning costs.

However, as in the Kenyan Green Belt Movement, other less tangible benefits are a prime goal of TreePeople. The program goes far beyond the planting of trees for mere environmental reasons to the TreePeople's philosophy of empowerment through personal action. "People really want to count," Andy Lipkis said. "They're crying out to make a difference. Planting a tree becomes an incredible expression of one's power." The group's goal is to turn people on to their ability to heal the world.

TreePeople did not begin with such lofty goals. Andy Lipkis, who does not have a degree in biology, started planting trees as an urban fifteen-year-old with no money, contacts, or particular talents. "He was just a regular schmo and he saw a problem," Katie Lipkis said. He responded with a simple action and a lot of determination. The feeling of empowerment and personal satisfaction that tree planting brought him are now the motivating forces behind TreePeople. "We keep seeing the example replicated," she said. "All the radical talk about empowerment is just recording our experience."

Katie Lipkis, who is Australian, joined the campaign in 1983 after meeting Andy Lipkis when he came to speak in Melbourne. Never having planted a tree before, she moved to Los Angeles, married him, and became TreePeople's director of development. "With ten years of experience in the advertising business, I came in as the big bad bully," she said. "My role was to be the pushy tough

TreePeople volunteers take a break from their urban planting efforts. (Photograph by Ben Swets)

one, to be a hard-ass. Her tactics have boosted the group's annual budget to $2 million. By 1992, TreePeople grew to a staff of thirty-six, with more than 18,000 members and 500 volunteers.

The work has been exhausting, though, and Katie Lipkis said she and her husband are "becoming less and less involved in the daily activities." They hired a manager to take over the operation to leave them free to tackle other problems. Andy Lipkis "has such an amazing vision and ability to solve problems," she said, "and he's starting to feel tied down by the constraints of TreePeople." They both would like to pursue more activities like the "Fruit Trees for Africa" effort that TreePeople carried out in 1985, when famine in Africa made international headlines.

TreePeople had been distributing nursery-surplus fruit trees in California and discovered that some of the species could adapt to certain African climates. They airlifted more than 5,000 trees to fourteen villages in Kenya, Ethiopia, Tanzania, and Cameroon. The trees produced leaves within weeks of planting, and most produced fruit in their first year. A project manager visited each village twice a year to teach horticultural techniques and home economics, giving the villagers the ability to dry and cook fruit, make jams and pies, and sell them to neighboring villages. They have also set up commercial nurseries, grafting new trees from the original stock.

"Our real passion is with people rather than nature," Katie Lipkis explained. "People are powerful enough to destroy something but also powerful enough to build it back up again. In the healing of our planet we heal people, and you can't really do one without the other."

5

Wild Places

The rainforest. For those of us who live far from its dense darkness and teeming life, the image holds a magic place in our minds. For those who live within the shelter of its canopy, it provides home, health, and livelihood. For many on its fringes, it is the last obstacle of nature to be conquered, a barrier to economic growth.

"There is something in the human past that makes us respond to the rainforest, something in the human spirit that seems to need to know about wild places," says Catherine Caufield, an American writer who won the Global 500 award in 1988 for her book *In the Rainforest: Report from a Strange, Beautiful, Imperiled World.*

Published in January 1985 in the United Kingdom and the United States, it has since been translated into Spanish, Portuguese, German, Japanese, Bahasa Indonesian, Bulgarian, Estonian, and other languages. Caufield still gets letters from readers, and she said that they "get terribly moved" by her book. *In the Rainforest* chronicles the ongoing destruction of the world's tropical forests. The tragedy is that no two rainforests are alike; each contains a unique catalogue of plants and animals—not to mention people—that coexist

> *My dream is to see this forest conserved because we know it can guarantee the future of all the people who live in it. Not only that, I believe that in a few years the Amazon can become an economically viable region not only for us, but for the whole planet . . . I don't want flowers at my funeral because I know they would be taken from the forest. . . .*
>
> —*Chico Mendes*

in a complex, delicate ecological balance. No one even knows how many species each forest holds. Overall, tropical rainforests are estimated to contain about 50 percent of the Earth's insects, animals, and plants, but only about 10 percent of them have been identified. At current rates of destruction, many species may be wiped out before scientists have a chance to even name them, let alone discover their potential contributions to medicine, diet, and world commerce.

Caufield's book offers an engrossing blend of facts, folklore, biology, ecology, history, and cultural background, interspersed with quotes from scientists, ranchers, government officials, and indigenous forest dwellers around the world. The research, which consumed four years of Caufield's life, took her to rainforests in Australia, Brazil, Colombia, Costa Rica, Indonesia, New Guinea, Panama, and the Philippines.

Caufield herself had never been in a rainforest before she started the book. She had studied ethnobiology and was an environmental correspondent for *New Science* magazine in London, but her only real knowledge of rainforests was gleaned from a radio news report. It was in 1972, at the time of the Stockholm conference, the first major international meeting to discuss implications of global environmental problems. Caufield was driving alone from Philadelphia to New York City on a rainy night when she heard on the radio that scientists had announced the rainforest was being destroyed at an alarming rate.

An idea flashed through her mind: "I thought, 'I must go there! I'll just explain how bad this is and people will listen.' " But, like all best intentions in a busy world, the thought was pushed to the back of her mind and she forgot all about the forests.

Several years later, Earthscan, a British publisher specializing in books on development and the environment, asked her to write a short booklet on rainforest destruction. The general approach at the time was focused only on the endangered animal life of the forests, not on the human and political context. But after writing the booklet Caufield realized there was a much bigger story to be told.

Her research began in Panama, where she walked in a tropical rainforest for the first time. "I had high expectations that it would be completely foreign, exotic, wild—and it was," she recalled, remembering especially the constant racket of the howler monkeys. She was in the company of scientists who were able to explain the workings of the forest and point out subtleties of plant and animal life that she would otherwise have missed.

Her experiences in writing the book disturbed her deeply, as she noted the "steady curve of destruction in four years of research." Her book documents the combined pressures that threaten the survival of the forests:

> A few thousand years ago the rainforest belt covered 5 billion acres—14 percent of the earth's land surface. Man has already destroyed half that. Most of the damage has been done in the last two hundred years, especially since the end of the Second World War. Now Latin America has 57 percent of the remaining rainforest. Southeast Asia and the Pacific islands have 25 percent. And West Africa has 18 percent.
>
> . . . Why are these forests—the richest, oldest, most complex eco-systems on earth—being cut down at such a rate? Why destroy a forest? To sell its timber, to get at the gold and iron underneath, to get more land for agriculture. There are psychological motives too: the wish to conquer nature, the fear of the unknown, nationalistic and strategic desires to occupy uncontrolled regions.

Decades of Destruction

The United Nations Food and Agriculture Organization (FAO) estimates that from 1981 to 1990, Africa lost 4.8 million hectares a year, or 1.7 percent, of its total forest land, Asia 4.7 million hectares or 1.4 percent, and Latin America 7.3 million hectares or 0.9 percent. Tropical forests disappeared at the rate of 16.8 million hectares a year between 1981 and 1990. 1990 figures show an 80 percent increase in destruction over the previous decade. Many authorities believe even these figures are drastically underreported.

In a lengthy phone coversation, we asked Caufield which of the competing interests in the tropical forests poses the biggest threat. Although it varies from place to place, she said, the construction of large dams to generate electricity is perhaps the most insidious. The flooding created upstream from the dams destroys animals, plants, and indigenous villages; the provision of water for irrigation encourages further local destruction; and the disruption of natural water flows destroys river systems and coastal estuarine systems far beyond the actual dam site.

The problems seem insurmountable, the destruction already too widespread to save the rich biological treasures of the Earth that the rainforests represent. But Caufield still has hope for the situation. "Don't be too easily discouraged," she said. "You have to be willing to just fight the good fight. You can't fight a generalized battle. It has to be fought individually. You win fighting for a place that you care about."

Caufield sits on the board of the Rainforest Action Network, a grass-roots group that works with local communities and organizations in more than sixty countries to pressure corporations, governments, aid agencies, and banks to stop funding projects that destroy tropical rainforests. But she warns her fellow Americans that "if we don't act here, we really can't act elsewhere" because we will lack credibility. That is why she has "made it a point to be involved in organizations working on domestic issues too." Some of her articles for the *New Yorker* have dealt with issues of Native Americans and destruction of the forest in the American Northwest.

"People need a deeper understanding" of the rainforest and of all environmental issues, Caufield believes. That is where she sees her role as a journalist: "To make information that's complicated, obscure and hard to get, understandable." And although she sees her work as important, she is very modest about her individual contribution. Like others who communicate information, she does not feel she's "doing something" in the sense that other Global 500 winners "do" projects.

"I've never even told anybody I've won it," she admitted. "How do you drop it into a conversation? I've told my mother about it. She was thrilled." In the first few years after she received the award, she said, nobody knew what it was all about. But as she has become increasingly involved in conservation efforts, she has run into other environmentalists who have also received the recognition.

Another modest but highly effective rainforest preservationist is botanical artist Margaret Mee. Her paintings, acclaimed by botanists and art critics alike, have brought to viewers around the world the beauty and fragility of the Amazonian jungle flora. In voluminous diaries she kept during sketching trips into the forest, what shines through is an unlikely mix of gentility and passion for the rainforests she painted. Her paintings, too, reflect this combination

Suri Indian children watch a bulldozer destroy part of their land in the Amazon. (Photograph © by Mark Edwards/Still Pictures)

in the delicate artistry of the floral figures against the dark and tangled backdrop of the forest.

Mee made her first trip into the Amazon rainforest in 1956, at the age of forty-nine. The British 1989 laureate was to return fourteen times before being killed in a traffic accident in England in 1988, at the age of eighty-one.

During her trips she discovered at least eight new plant species, four of which are named after her. Her collection of more than 400 watercolor compositions, 15 diaries, and 25 sketchbooks is credited with being the most extensive record of Amazonian plants ever created. Some of her paintings could end up being the only record of plants and flowers that may become extinct if their habitat is destroyed.

Mee painted only from living plants, not dried specimens, and what distinguishes her work from other botanical artists' is her scientific accuracy, exquisite composition, and use of true color.

Her interest in plants can be traced to her father, an amateur naturalist who could identify many wild plants. As a young child she collected flowers near her family's home in England and sketched them. Another important influence was her grandfather, a frequent traveler who used to regale the family with stories from afar.

Mee left her job teaching art in Liverpool in 1932 to move to Germany, and only returned to painting in 1945, soon after World War II. Although she had studied art since the age of seventeen, it was during these years, studying at various studios and schools in London, that she acquired her skills of observation and detail.

In 1952 she had an opportunity to travel again when she learned that her sister, who lived in São Paulo, Brazil, was gravely ill. Mee and her husband Greville went to care for her, planning to stay for several years. They never left.

In São Paulo, Mee took a job teaching art at a local school. Her husband worked as a commercial artist. On weekends they would go walking in the densely vegetated areas outside the exploding city. One day Mee spotted a castor oil plant and was drawn by its curious fruits and leaves. She sat down to sketch it right away, and from then on immersed herself in sketching and painting flowers.

After exploring and painting much of the area surrounding São Paulo, the indomitable Mee was ready to delve into the Amazon jungle. On her first trip she was accompanied by a fellow art teacher who had often taken trips with the Mees closer to home. Burdened with clothes, tubes of paint, sketchbooks, and a revolver, the two women took off for a month, flying into Belém, a city near the mouth of the Amazon, 3,200 kilometers from São Paulo. An anthropologist working at the Goeldi Museum offered them the use of a thatched hut in a town on the Gurupi river. Hearing of their trip, a local botanist asked Mee to look for a particular vine reported to grow in that area. So the women set off on the arduous journey.

As they traveled by boat up the river, they slept in hammocks on the shore. "On the first night we hung our hammocks from the trees beside an enchanted lake," Mee wrote in her diary. "I could not sleep for listening to the magic sounds of the forest. Only the trees were silent, while the lake was alive with sparkling, splashing fishes, and the frogs' chorus mingled with the plaintive cries of night birds."

The pair endured hunger, intense heat, and what were for them quite primitive conditions. But they painted extensively. Of the return trip, Mee wrote, "When we reached Belém by train, São Paulo and smart summer dresses were only twelve hours away, though now Amazonia was in my blood. Murutucum, that haven of green peace, seemed to be the other side of the planet, but I knew I would return."

In her later years Mee increasingly spoke out about the destruction of the rainforest. In a magazine interview not long before her death, she said, "The last journey nearly broke my heart. All the way up the Rio Negro the forest had been burnt for charcoal. The land is useless for agriculture, so they simply cut it down and burned it. After that there's nothing. We went through miles and miles of blackened tree stumps where a few years ago there was primeval forest. It can never grow back. . . . Then there are the dams; vast areas of forest are disappearing under hydroelectric schemes. These bring no benefit to the people who live in Amazonia. It is a terrible tragedy. What can I do? There are so many flowers left to paint."

On what was to be her final trip, in 1988, she recounted in her diary how she painted the Amazon moonflower, a scarlet and green flower that blossoms only once, at night, between April and June. She had been searching for the elusive flower since she first glimpsed one while exploring the Rio Negro in 1965.

Back on the Negro, she had found an accessible bud to revisit in darkness. Sitting in a chair on the bow of a boat, she and several companions waited hours for it to bloom. In wonder they watched it unfold, and while Mee painted they hoped to witness the arrival of the pollinator, which, on the basis of the intensely scented flower's shape, was believed to be a large moth or a bat. "Our vigil was long," she wrote, "and I conclude that our intrusion had deterred the pollinator, upsetting the delicate balance between the plant and the animal that has taken millions of years to evolve.

"Our intrusion on the life of the moonflower was minor in comparison with what I have seen happening along the Amazon waterways, for the forest has changed considerably and the lovely plants I have painted along the Negro have disappeared. I can remember my excitement on my first journey there, when I moored my boat to a swartzia tree, full of perfumed white flowers, among the great trees on the banks. The changes have been disastrous, and the destruction and burning of the forests arouse fears for the future of our planet."

> *Of course, one of the worst things that goes along with the loss of the forests is the extinction of a quarter of all plants and animals on earth during the next 30 years. And that means, since we ultimately base civilization and productivity on our ability to use them, that we're throwing away very genuine opportunities. Yet it's very hard to realize that. Ultimately, things like intensification of the greenhouse effect, the depletion of ozone, the pollution of the oceans, the lack of any place to put waste,...will force us to look at this unstable situation. America continues to receive large numbers of immigrants and to give aid to politically unstable countries in Latin and Central America, and needs to address larger ecological issues impacting the world we live in. We can't take off into space, so we need to conserve what we have here on earth.*
>
> ***—Peter Raven,***
> ***Director of Missouri Botanical Garden***
> ***Global 500 laureate***

Like Mee, many other environmentalists are motivated by a concern for future generations. Global 500 laureate Aila Keto shares the fear, and the passion, for the rainforests of the world.

By all accounts, Keto is a formidable footsoldier on the environmental front, armed with intellect, energy, and a zealous commitment to the cause. The crusading Australian is perhaps best known for her thorough studies of Queensland's Wet Tropics, an area of about one million hectares in northeast Queensland that had come under pressure from the timber industry. Keto was instrumental in getting the area designated as a World Heritage site, adding it to the many other natural and cultural sites around the world deemed by the United Nations Educational, Scientific and Cultural Organization (UNESCO) as places of universal value and therefore safeguarded from development.

To assess the merits of the nomination, the World Heritage Commission in 1984 asked Keto to document the biological value of this particular rainforest. In her intensive six-month study, Keto divided the area into eighty-seven sections and painstakingly recorded the myriad plant, animal, and vegetation types found there. This information was catalogued in a computer database and presented in a 2,400-page report on the biological value of the region.

The study—the first ever conducted of the Wet Tropics—determined that the area had one of the highest concentrations of ancient plant species in the world, dating back millions of years to the age when Australia was part of a huge continent—with what are now Africa, South America, Antarctica, and India—called Gondwanaland. Keto described the area as "the evolutionary cradle for much of the earth's biological diversity."

Keto says Queensland's rainforests provide the only link with species that existed at that time and thus offer an important bridge to understanding future life on Earth. "The surviving rainforest plants are part of a gene pool which will be vital—particularly when man-made climatic change occurs—to the continuation of species," she said. "Rainforests are an integral part of our survival strategy." In December 1988, after much debate, the World Heritage Commission added the Queensland's Wet Tropics to its list of protected areas, thereby closing the area to commercial logging.

Keto's focus on nature dates back to her childhood in El-Arish, a sawmill town in the shadow of the rainforest. On trips home during the years she spent at the University of Queensland earning a masters degree and a doctorate in biochemistry, she witnessed the gradual disappearance of vegetation. Then she heard a lecture by renowned biologist Peter Raven, director of the Missouri Botanical Garden in the United States and also a Global 500 laureate. His words had a lasting effect on the emerging environmentalist. "For the first time I saw the Earth as going beyond the here and now, going back millions of years," Keto said. "That affected me and still does."

Her concern prompted her in 1982 to found the Rainforest Conservation Society (RCS), the first organization in Australia devoted entirely to the protection of rainforests. Working with her husband, biochemist Keith Scott, she established headquarters in her Brisbane home—set in a small pocket of tropical forest—and began her campaign to apply scientific disciplines to conservation.

She took up a mind-boggling schedule of research, public lectures, debates, participation in committees, delegations, conferences, and inquiries, trying to communicate the results of her impeccable research to scientific professionals, politicians, and the public. She figures that during one decade of unpaid labor, working sixteen hours a day, seven days a week, she equalled about twenty to thirty years of "normal" work.

The relentless effort has paid off. In addition to the Wet Tropics' World Heritage designation, she has been instrumental in halting mining activities proposed for the McIlwraith Range, on Australia's Cape York Peninsula. In a national park proposal for the area, she evaluated its biological, biogeographical, and anthropological significance and found it second only to the Wet Tropics for concentrations of rare and threatened plant and animal species left over from the Gondwanic age.

Fraser Island and the Great Sandy Region, the subject of another RCS study, was also nominated for World Heritage listing, with a recommendation that logging in the region be phased out within six months. Her field work there disputed the true sustainability of "sustained yield" logging, a theory used to promote selective timber harvesting in tropical forests throughout the world. The theory assumed that harvesting of a limited number of trees within a given area would not disrupt its overall ecology. Keto showed that, in fact, the practice was unsustainable not only ecologically but economically, too.

In another study, on energy and tropical forests, Keto determined that tropical deforestation is contributing to the "greenhouse effect." Trees absorb carbon dioxide from the air. When a tree is felled, its accumulation of carbon dioxide is released into the atmosphere and it can no longer absorb the gas, which has been linked to global warming. Keto found that the rate of tropical deforestation as of late 1991 was responsible for as much as 30 percent of global carbon dioxide emissions.

Although Keto's conservation efforts are admired by many,

they have also won her enemies. She has suffered animosity, and even death threats, from loggers who believe she is depriving them of their livelihood. But Keto does not flinch. "As in so many other places," she said, "the loggers had mined out their resource and faced inevitable job losses as the industry collapsed. Plantations are the only solution. Instead of fighting conservation, the Queensland Government should provide a desperately needed lead in reforestation and tropical plantation development."

However, Keto struggles with the fact that "the Government applauds those who build up an economic empire based on competition and greed, yet when somebody does something that will ultimately benefit everyone, they are treated suspiciously."

The benefits of reforestation to loggers and other citizens, she argues, are manifold. The application of appropriate management principles she pioneered will ultimately result in more jobs, not fewer. And people will benefit from properly managed use of other forest resources, too. There is one chance in four that medications and pharmaceuticals come directly or indirectly from tropical forests. And more than 1,000 tropical forest plants contain chemicals active against cancer.

Despite the difficult years behind her, Keto clearly has more fight left in her. On an international level, she plans to develop ecologically sustainable methods to manage tropical forests. On the home front, the RCS will explore the viablity of mixed-species tree plantations that simulate natural forests.

Another major effort will be directed at educating the public about the importance of protecting the rainforests. "I look at the human species as just one of many millions of species on this earth," Keto said. "We are late-comers, and we are causing extraordinary destruction. We are capable of bringing about the end of the evolutionary era that has been the basis of the tremendous biological diversity we have now. Rainforests are a window into our evolutionary past and a window into the future. Before rainforests, we had much simpler ecosystems. The beginning of rainforests was a quantum leap."

Like Keto, Brazilian rubber tapper Francisco Mendes Filho fought to defend the rainforests of his native country and was threatened many times with death. For him, those threats were borne out. Mendes, better known as Chico, was shot and killed as he stepped out his back door one day after years of conflict with local

Chico Mendes

cattle ranchers over his efforts to save his people, his job, and the forest he lived in.

In a book entitled *Fight for the Forest: Chico Mendes in His Own Words,* the 1987 laureate traced the beginning of trouble to the early 1970s, when the government halted subsidies on Amazon rubber estates. Owners abandoned their forested properties or sold them to cattle ranchers, who started clearing them for pasture.

The struggle began as a fight against the eviction of rubber tappers, but as the rainforests were cut down it evolved into a battle against deforestation. Mendes fought the battle by helping found a rubber tappers union, the Xapuri Rural Workers Union, in 1977. The union sent bands of villagers into the forests to confront the ranchers' men who were cutting the trees. The union spawned the idea of "extractive reserves" in which "the land is under public ownership but the rubber tappers and other workers who live on that land should have the right to live and work there."

The cause drew widespread support from international environmental organizations such as the U.S. Environmental Defense Fund (EDF), which opposes destructive forest projects. Bruce Rich, the EDF's International Director and also a Global 500 winner, helped Mendes lobby the U.S. Congress and the multilateral development banks, which were funding road building into the Amazon, during Mendes' 1985 visit to Washington, D.C. The effort boosted international support for the rubber tappers and contributed to the establishment of more than fifteen extractive reserves.

Throughout his leadership, Mendes felt the pressure of battle. "After each stage in the struggle," he said, "we evaluate the situation, we learn from our experiences. The struggle teaches us many things. Every day we learn something, while at the same time knowing we could be on the receiving end of a bullet at any time."

In December 1988, a bullet did come for Mendes, but it could not stop the momentum of his campaign to conserve the rainforests. The EDF set up the Chico Mendes Fund to raise money for the

National Council of Rubber Tappers' campaigns for extractive reserves, community development projects, and alliances with other forest peoples. Spurred on by Mendes' assassination and the spotlight it threw on rainforest issues, organizations around the world have rallied to safeguard the wealth that the forests represent.

6

On the Edge of Extinction

The survival of African rhinoceroses, Caribbean parrots, and a wide variety of other endangered species depends on the maintenance of their special habitat. This equation is no less true for the estimated 200 million indigenous people around the world, and indeed for all cultures of the world no matter what their level of "civilization."

The destruction of rainforests is the main threat to indigenous people throughout the tropics. It is estimated in Brazil alone that Amazonian Indian tribes have disappeared at the rate of one per year throughout the twentieth century. After much pressure from international environmental groups, the Brazilian government in 1992 began setting aside tracts of land as tribal reserves. Still, many Indian supporters believe the parcels are far too small to ensure the survival of their inhabitants' traditional ways. Tribal rights activists acknowledge that the choice between traditional tribal life and modern civilization must be made by the Indians themselves, but they argue that if current rates of cultural disappearance continue, there will be no time left to decide.

Among the tribes on the very edge of extinction are Brazil's Kayapo Indians, who in 1991 numbered 6,000 people. They call themselves "The People of the Water's Source," referring to their homeland on the banks of the Xingu, a tributary of the Amazon. But this land is being systematically invaded by ranchers, miners, and loggers seeking to carry away the rainforest's wealth for their own and their country's economic advancement. In the process, they destroy the ecosystem that supports the tribal people's way of life. As if this were not bad enough, they also bring diseases that decimate the Indians, who have no natural immunity to the foreign germs.

Global 500 laureate Paulino Payakan is leading the Kayapo in a battle against the European colonial descendants and their concept of development, hoping to preserve his people's forest shelter and thus their very existence.

"When I was still a young boy I wanted to see the world," Payakan recalled in an interview for the film *Without Borders*, produced by Global 500 laureate Barbara Pyle for the Turner Broadcasting System. So he left his village of Goratiri and struck out for the edge of the forest to work with Brazil's "white people," mining gold and logging timber. But after seeing the destruction this wrought on the forest and the pollution it dumped in the water, he said, "I ran from the white man. I ran from their machinery and their gold."

Fleeing the modern world, he returned to Goratiri, where "my people did not understand the great threat to us and the problem that was coming." He remembers thinking, "If they kill the forest, we will die. We must leave here." He convinced his people of the danger and led them sixty-four kilometers upriver away from the threat. There they established a new village, called Aukre.

The Kayapo, whose ancestors have lived in the Amazon for more than 2,000 years, set up life all over again. Their daily survival depends upon careful use of the forest's bounty, and they carried the practices of their old home into their new land.

> *The forest has inspired flights of fancy since the search for the fountain of youth almost 500 years ago, but information on the potential value of the forest as a source of medicinal plants is scanty and largely anecdotal. No one pays indigenous peoples for traditional knowledge that leads to identification of new compounds from nature. Amazonia holds the world's largest store of species. Deforestation destroys both the compounds themselves and the traditional knowledge of medicinal uses of each plant.*
>
> ***—Philip Fearnside***
> ***Research professor***
> ***Dept. of Ecology,***
> ***National Institute for***
> ***Research in the Amazon***
> ***Global 500 laureate***

They plant crops to blend with existing vegetation, leaving trees to protect soil from the sun and rain. Vegetable ashes are used to fertilize the topsoil. They also fish the rivers employing centuries-old techniques. For example, a group of adult men wade into the river beating bundles of a particular vine on the water's surface. This causes the vines to release a chemical that removes oxygen from the water, immobilizing fish and making it easy for young boys downstream to pluck them out.

Over the centuries of life in the rainforest, the Kayapo have discovered the value to humans of the surrounding plant and animal species. Anita Roddick, a Global 500 laureate and founder of the Body Shop (see page 104), who roams the world searching for natural cosmetic recipes, visited the Kayapo to collect oils, seeds, and natural food dyes to convert into cosmetic products to sell in her stores. She found that the Kayapo "have categorized ninety-five different types of dysentery and have a plant that will cure each one of them." Scientists are studying traditional tribal medicines for commercialization, and are even exploring a possible cure for cancer.

The Kayapo want to maintain this symbiotic relationship with nature that has sustained their tribe over so many generations. "Our origins are very dear to us," Payakan explained. "It is important that we preserve our traditions. We want to remain Indians."

But the inexorable commercial forces that drove the tribe from Goratiri soon threatened their newly established home. Aware that the tribe could not just keep moving, Payakan left the village again. This time he headed to Belém, at the Amazon's mouth, to fight the invaders on their own turf.

There he learned Portuguese, the country's language of law and politics; carefully observed Brazilians' customs and technology; and rallied support from the country's biologists, anthropologists, and environmentalists.

Armed with a better understanding of what his people were up against, Payakan mobilized them for a political fight. In early 1989 he organized a meeting in Altamira protesting a large-scale dam project, the Kararao. The government believes the hydroelectric dam is necessary to provide energy for the nation's 144 million people, but opponents point out that it will flood 18,000 square kilometers of rainforest, including the Kayapo's home. Payakan also led a march of tribal members in Brasilia to protest damaging government practices. "The government defends destruction," he claimed. "I defend the forest."

Back in Aukre, he is trying to convince some of his own people that the rainforest is more profitable standing than cut down. He has started projects to harvest Brazil nuts for sale, and is trying to band the Kayapo leaders together to use their land for other such income-generating projects rather than sell it off to goldminers and lumbermen for short-term profits.

Payakan's vision, however, was at odds with the government's dedication to opening up Brazil's interior at all costs, and he was arrested on a charge of interfering in the country's domestic affairs. To undermine the authority of tribal spokesmen like Payakan, a law was passed stating that an Indian who spoke Portuguese rather than his tribal tongue could no longer be considered an Indian. The law was eventually overturned, but the obstacles to rainforest protection remained.

Borrowing a technique from the encroaching society, Payakan documented the forest destruction on videotape to rally support for his people's campaign. He also recorded the Kayapo's rituals and everyday life. If all else fails, at least the tribe's descendants will have a record of their people's traditional ways.

"If there were no forest, there would be no Indians," Payakan told an international conference meeting in Belém. "We have learned about you, now it's time for you to learn about us."

Another threatened tribal culture is that of the Lacandon Indians of Mexico's Chiapas State. Their characteristic features—prominent noses, round faces, and thick lips—could adorn the pillars of an ancient Mayan city. The shoeless Indians are living remnants of that great Middle American civilization, which built monumental cities and produced astonishing architectural, astronomical, and mathematical achievements before mysteriously collapsing between 700 and 900 A.D.

The Lacandon civilization is under threat from progressing development, but they have an ally in Global 500 laureate Gertrude Duby Blom, who has struggled for half a century to save their way of life. She was more discouraged at the age of ninety, when we spoke with her at the 1991 Stockholm awards ceremony, than when she began the battle.

"I am a failure," said the Swiss-born journalist. "Just look at their jungle. It has been cut down by lumbermen, invaded by land-

Kayapo Indians have lived in the Amazon for more than 2,000 years. (Photograph © by Mark Edwards/Still Pictures)

less *campesinos* and replaced by cattle. Man is so irresponsible. Someday we will all disappear."

Blom first learned of the Lacandones in 1940 while traveling to Mexico by boat. In Europe Blom had made her mark as an effective socialist organizer, marrying and divorcing two husbands in the process. Fearing for her safety as a result of her outspoken opposition to fascism, she prudently sought safe haven in Mexico from Nazi Germany's expanding control of Europe. On the long voyage she read the book *Mexique, Terre Indienne* (*Mexico, Indian Land*), by Jacques Soustelle, a famous French anthropologist and controversial postwar political figure.

It was not until 1943 that Blom had the time and opportunity to enter the Chiapan jungle—Lacandon country. A pioneering government expedition, headed by Danish explorer Frans Blom, was examining the remote region and agreed to let her join them as a journalist and photographer. "This jungle filled me with a sense of wonder that has never left me," she later wrote. A woman given to advocacy and absolutes, she assumed the cause of protecting the jungle and its people with the passion she had once reserved for antifascism in Europe.

Not only did Blom find her life's cause on the Chiapan expedition; she fell in love with Frans Blom, a scientist who had made many significant Mayan discoveries. They married shortly after.

The Bloms returned to Chiapas in 1948 for a seven-month expedition that led to their important two-volume study, *La Selva Lacandona* (*The Lacandon Jungle*). While her husband furthered his reputation by making two important archaeological finds, Trudi Blom pursued her interest in the ruins' living history, the Lacandones.

In 1952 the couple bought a large house in the then-isolated Chiapan town of San Cristobal de las Casas. *Na-Bolom* (Jaguar House), as it was named, quickly became a way station for archaeologists exploring the region's Mayan ruins. Later, it became a guest house for selected tourists off the beaten path. But most importantly, it became Blom's headquarters for establishing her relationship with the Indians.

With the confidence and conviction that she brought to all issues, Blom penetrated the Lacandon society—and was accepted. The determined journalist with important friends became a single-minded advocate for the Lacandones' cause. She collected at *Na-*

Bolom a library of materials on the Lacandon people and their ancient culture that she made available to anyone who was interested. She also established a nursery to help replant the trees being felled, a problem that was especially troubling for the Lacandon because of their belief that the sky will fall and the world will end if a tree is cut without seeking their god's permission.

Despite her achievements, Blom has berated herself for not better defending the Indians. "My life is full of lost battles," she said in a film on her life, "but the spirit of the fight is still in me."

Only about 400 Lacandones still practice the tribe's traditional ways. But whatever the fate of the people themselves, the world of these Mayan descendants will be preserved forever through the thousands of photographs Blom took during her fifty-year fight.

Although she stoutly maintains that she is "not a photographer," the pictures she took document the innocent, harmonious life of the Lacandones before their home was attacked by the chain saws of lumbermen, the bulldozers of cattlemen, and the crude slash-and-burn agriculture of landless *campesinos.* The photographs also dramatically capture the wanton destruction of the forest itself.

In putting together an exhibit of her photography in 1984, Alex Harris, director of the Center for Documentary Photography at Duke University, noted: "As more and more of the jungle disappears, the message becomes more strident, and more difficult to ignore. In her old age, Blom has come to resemble the Old Testament prophet who cries, not in the wilderness, but for it; meanwhile, the pace of destruction quickens, with no end in sight."

Throughout history there are instances of great civilizations crumbling, and they usually leave behind some concrete sign of previous glory. As the monumental cities in the Chiapas jungle bear silent witness to the bygone greatness of the Mayas, the Acropolis of Athens, whose ruins overlook the modern city, attests to the lost splendor of ancient Greece. But these stone remnants are themselves under threat from forces unimagined in times past.

Laureate Thodoros Skoulikidis, an energetic Greek chemical engineer, is devoting his life to saving the classic citadel. Constructed mostly during the time of Pericles, who died in 429 B.C., the Acropolis has through the years suffered war, looting, accidental destruction, and the ravages of time. But now an insidious vandal, industrial pollution, increasingly threatens the architectural masterpiece.

Thodoros Skoulikidis

"Just look how the smog hangs over Athens," Skoulikidis said as he escorted us one hot August day among the ruins of the Pantheon, the architectural marvel that crowns the Acropolis. "I am a realist," he continued. "There are limits to what you can do to halt pollution. Half the country's population and half of the nation's industry is found in Athens. Sixty percent of all the country's automobiles are here, too. To add to all this, Athens suffers from thermal inversions that form a blanket of pollution over it."

The gritty air that burns the eyes and has turned Athens' once-fabled blue sky into an ominous grey also eats away the stone monuments. Skoulikidis, a university professor, points out the damage with a beautician's eye. The eroded head of a statue, he noted, looks more like a death mask than the finely chiseled and lifelike representation it once was. In some places it is easy to see that at least an inch of the original surface has been lost to corrosion.

Some steps have been taken to control the damage. Buses are no longer allowed access to the top of the Acropolis hill. Only solar and electrical energy can be used for central heating in the zone around the monuments. In the future, only electrical cars will be allowed in the monument zone. And it is illegal now to use fuel with more than 1 percent of sulfur anywhere in Athens.

Efforts to maintain the monuments are not new. "Previously, architects, archaeologists, civil engineers, and government officials ran the maintenance and restoration of the monuments," Skoulikidis noted. Major restorations were made from 1837–1842, using steel clamps and junctions embedded in lead. More than 100 tons of reinforced concrete were poured into the Acropolis from 1900–1935. But the limited knowledge of the time led to some mistakes. For example, the inserted steel clamps expanded and broke the marble. Nevertheless, the restoration work generally held up until the 1970s.

It was then that the destructive impact of Athens' expanding industry, established following World War II and the subsequent Greek Civil War, became painfully apparent. In 1975, Skoulikidis was appointed to the Committee for the Preservation of the Acropolis Monument. The German-trained professor at Athens' National Technical University brought a much-needed chemist's perspective to the worsening pollution problem.

Skoulikidis called for a complete rethinking of the approach to long-term preservation of the ruins. Scientists compared old photographs and measurements, and statues reproduced from old molds, to the current structures. They estimated that the damage from industrial pollution had increased 30 percent. It turned out that quick fixes such as the heralded new organic and inorganic coatings used abroad had actually accelerated destruction.

Skoulikidis promoted a prudent strategy. Some vulnerable artifacts were taken to a museum for special protection, and others were given added protection *in situ*. In addition, the committee lobbied for antipollution laws in Athens, whose population in 1992 was approaching 3.5 million. Skoulikidis argued that the dynamics of the damage to the Acropolis were so complex that scientists had to doublecheck every assumption they held.

The Committee for the Preservation of the Acropolis is now engaged in the long process of instituting a new preservation and restoration regime. Titanium, a strong, light metal that expands at about the same rate as marble, has been substituted for steel in junctions. New protective coatings for marble and limestone are being carefully tested. The Acropolis steps have been covered by wood floorboards to protect them from the endless tramping of tourists' feet. Valuable statues are being taken out of the smoggy open elements in favor of indoor museum viewing.

Over the past decades Skoulikidis has learned the hard way that old methods are inadequate to protect Greece's cultural heritage from industrial pollution, and new techniques must be continually pioneered. "There is limited knowledge abroad about our specific problems," he noted while looking out from the commanding vantage of the Acropolis. "We must do our own research. Finding solutions will take time and patience."

7

Spreading the Word

It takes courage to be an investigative environmental reporter, especially in the Third World. In many countries, spotlighting a problem suggests government corruption and neglect, and journalists who pursue such stories are viewed as almost subversive. Nondemocratic governments pushing unsustainable national development or individuals profiting at the expense of the environment are quite capable of taking extreme measures to quash a revealing story. In Asia, for example, journalists have been subjected to bruises and broken bones because of stories detailing environmental abuses.

So Third World journalists often operate at great personal risk. In Thailand, one reporter we visited in downtown Bangkok told us about the dangers she faces. Global 500 laureate Normita Thongtham writes a bi-weekly column on the environment for the daily *Bangkok Post*, the nation's leading English-language newspaper. The column, titled "Nature Notebook," deals with a wide range of environmental topics, from deforestation to water pollution to toxic waste. Thongtham frequently takes on local politicians and other figures of power in this rapidly industrializing country.

For example, in one story she challenged a proposed dam project that would have flooded a vast tract of virgin forest, the primary habitat of a bird on the World Heritage list of endangered species. She lambasted the influential Supreme Commander of the army for accepting the hospitality of the interested power company. Thongtham likened the dam project, which was eventually scrapped, to "destroying Solomon's temple to build condomini-

Normita Thongtham

ums." But Thongtham has to be careful of how she phrases her criticism. "If I see a minister doing something I don't like," she explained, "I attack him, but in a subtle way. If it's not subtle, I can get killed."

Thongtham, a Filipino by birth who has lived in Thailand for twenty-one years, came to the environmental beat in a very roundabout way. She used to accompany her Thai husband, a horticulture professor, on forays into the jungle to collect specimens. This led her, in 1982, to begin a column on gardening, and she continued her travels with him to write about forest flora. After repeated trips, she saw the forest was shrinking. She was troubled, but it was her husband who urged her to write about the changes. So she expanded the scope of her column to deal broadly with the environment. Though her main job at the *Bangkok Post* is editing and page layout, she manages to research and write her "Nature Notebook" every other Sunday.

Ironically, Thongtham's work has been made easier by so-called "natural disasters" such as typhoons and floods. She said these climatic occurences never used to strike Thailand because it was buffered by Vietnam's forests. Now they hit with full force. Death tolls are high partly because population growth has put more people on the land and partly because that land has been degraded by rampant deforestation. In particular, Thongtham cites flooding in 1988 that killed more than 300 people when cut logs stacked on mountain slopes were swept down by mudslides, crushing entire villages. "That awakened people," she said, to the need for environmental protection.

At that time, Thongtham wrote mostly about deforestation. With 2.5 percent of its forests disappearing every year throughout the 1980s, it is a major threat to Thailand's environment. She feels, nevertheless, that she has sufficiently educated Thais about deforestation to move on to other problems.

Air pollution has become the focus of many columns, and deservedly so. Bangkok's air stings the eyes, irritates the throat, and causes respiratory ailments. A pall of smog hangs over the huge city. At day's end soot covers all exposed surfaces, including clothing and skin. The problem is caused mainly by more than two million motor vehicles—which lack pollution control devices—clogging Bangkok's streets. Residents recommend not walking anywhere because of the discomfort, but the alternatives only add to the congestion. On our visit to meet with Thongtham it took us thirty-five minutes to go by taxi to an office we could have walked to in fifteen.

Water pollution is another growing problem. The Gulf of Thailand and its four major tributaries—the Chao Phya, Bang Pakong, Tha Chin, and Mae Klong—are choking on pollution caused by untreated domestic sewage, industrial waste, and residues from agricultural chemicals. In a December 1991 column, Thongtham wrote of a visit to the banks of the Chao Phya, within the city limits: "I inhaled deeply to fill my lungs with the incoming breeze, and successfully filled it with the putrid smell of sewage. I looked closely at the water: It was mucky and as dark as ink. . . . The water in Bangkok's *klongs* (canals) was once used for bathing, washing, and cooking, but now it is so polluted people have to cover their nose with a handkerchief when they walk past a *klong*."

The Population Bomb Ticks

The population explosion will come to an end before very long, but how? By human population control or human disaster? Most demographers don't take such an apocalyptic view as Paul and Anne Ehrlich, the celebrated American husband-and-wife team and Global 500 laureates. But the growth rate is truly astonishing, especially in less developed countries where 90 percent of the increase is projected to take place. It took all of human history until 1800 to reach the first billion mark, and only 130 more years to reach two billion. We are now adding one billion people every eleven years, a rate that will continue until at least the year 2020. Rapid population growth, against a backdrop of poverty, drives people to cut down forests, overuse marginal soils, and exhaust their nonrenewable resources just to survive. In rich countries, population growth coupled with higher per capita resource consumption has the same damaging results.

In writing about these issues, Thongtham addresses what she perceives as a lack of information, not only about local implications of environmental damage but also global ones. "Thai people are not aware of what other countries are doing about the environment," she explained. Accordingly, her well-documented articles compare air pollution in Bangkok to that in Mexico City, water pollution in Thailand's Chao Phya to that in London's Thames River, local toxic waste problems to those in the United States.

Her tirades do not target government alone. She continually exhorts individual citizens to be more aware of their own behavior. "People cause pollution," she wrote in one of her columns. "No matter what profession you are in, whether you are a doctor or a lawyer, a farmer or an industrialist, a teacher or a student, a taxi driver or a sidewalk vendor, you—all of us—cause pollution one way or another. We pollute by smoking, by driving cars with faulty engines or motorcycles whose engines have been tampered with, by littering, by dumping waste into the waterways, by using hairsprays and aerosols. We pollute in hundreds of ways, and only we can stop pollution."

Krisna Tamrakar

She urges people not just to be aware of the problem, but to become part of the solution. In her columns she lists specific actions her readers can take. "We have passed the environmental awareness stage," she said. "I want to see more action." As she tells her readers, "You may think that one person's contribution is very small, but Bangkok alone has a population of

> *We must help people to understand and appreciate their natural environment. If we are to achieve an enduring harmony between humanity and nature, it can only be through changing perceptions, understanding and belief. That, above all means communication.*
>
> ***—Salleh Mohd Nor***
> ***President, Malayan Nature Society***
> ***Global 500 laureate***

around seven million people, and if everyone pitches in, then think of what we can accomplish in cleaning up our air and water."

She also practices what she preaches. For example, Thongtham does not own a car herself, instead taking public buses—the only form of mass transportation in Bangkok—to get around. "How could I write about air pollution," she asked, "when I'm sitting comfortably in an air-conditioned car?"

One cannot help but feel moved after talking with her. She expresses both personal anguish and energy in her earnest words, and it is obvious she is committed to the issues she covers. Defining her approach, she said there are many environmental reporters in the country, "but they don't mix their personal feelings in their writings. I do."

The forty-five-year-old mother of two wishes she had more time to devote to her environmental writing, even though she does not know if her articles change anyone's behavior. It is "like needles trying to prick people," she complained. "Sometimes it seems useless, like I'm wasting my time. But then, if I stop, who will do the work?" Also, the mere fact of being cited for environmental writing means she has to continue. But that is fine by her, because she would not want to write about anything else.

Along with written pieces like Thongtham's, radio, too, can be a powerful force in raising environmental awareness, especially in Third World countries where literacy rates are low and communities are isolated. In Nepal, for example, radio reaches 60 to 80 percent of the population, which is largely uneducated and widely scattered throughout the mountainous country.

Global 500 laureate Krisna Tamrakar carries environmental information to the people over the air. She produces three fifteen-minute programs every week, covering a wide range of local and global issues. One program deals with general environmental topics. Another discusses the environment in the context of women's and children's health and hygiene. The third focuses on tourism and its effect on Nepal's fragile natural resource base.

This poor nation suffers greatly from ecological damage. Most of its 19.6 million people are rural subsistence farmers who rely on firewood for 98 percent of their cooking and heating needs. In the 1950s, forests covered about 60 percent of the land; by 1991, that figure was down to 17 percent. One estimate places the current annual rate of destruction at about 50,600 hectares—about nine times the size of Manhattan Island.

The problem is aggravated by the 100,000-plus trekkers who inundate the country each year to take in its dramatic beauty but often end up contributing to its destruction. They, too, burn precious wood for fuel, and also leave trails of toilet paper and empty tin cans along the hiking paths.

The rampant destruction of forest cover on the steep mountain slopes, coupled with heavy monsoon rains and the continuing uplift of these young mountains—in some spots at the rate of about half an inch per year—triggers massive landslides. Collapsing hillsides can take whole villages with them. With a 1991 population growth rate of 2.5 percent aggravating pressure on the mountain ecosystem, many farmers have fled to the Terai, Nepal's southern lowland along the Indian border. But this has proved no safe haven. Its rivers silt up from erosion of the deforested slopes upstream, and floods are an increasing hazard.

We met with Tamrakar in Kathmandu, Nepal's capital, in the office of another Nepalese laureate, Krishna Kumar Pandey. Known as K.K., he runs a national program, called Jara Juri, which is similar to the Global 500 award in that it recognizes successful environmental initiatives by villagers. Later at her comfortable home outside of the bustling town, Tamrakar spoke of her work.

Her radio programs, she said, are carefully tailored to the needs of her audience. Once a month she or one of her staff travels the country, often hiking for three or four days along steep muddy trails, to learn about the interests of people in remote communities. The people say they do not want to listen to interviews with high government officials; they want to hear about people like themselves, "people on the street."

To answer women's requests to learn about sanitation and health, a prime concern for people with scant access to doctors, Tamrakar often broadcasts information about UNICEF, the United

Nations Children's Fund. For children who want to hear sounds of animals from all over the world, she sometimes runs animal-identification contests. Winners get a T-shirt and a two-night stay in a lodge in Nepal's Royal Chitwan National Park, where they may see some of the animals—such as elephants, tigers, and rhinoceroses—that they hear on the air.

Children also want to hear other children speak, so Tamrakar occasionally brings them onto her program to ask other children, and adults, too, not to destroy their surroundings. She also started storytelling once a month. The stories, narrated by one of the best actors in Nepal, deal with such topics as wildlife, the weather, and birds, of which some 800 species live in Nepal.

The programs seem to be a great success, with broadcasts triggering 400 to 800 letters from listeners each month. Tamrakar, who studied broadcast journalism at the Voice of Germany in Munich and the BBC in London, would like to lengthen the programs to half-an-hour each. "Fifteen minutes is not enough" to cover all the important issues, she lamented.

But time and money pose a problem, she said. The sari-clad journalist from Nepal's upper class works full-time as editor and broadcaster of Nepal's national news. She started producing environmental programs in 1978, doing the work in her own free time. Her first program was called "Our Forest." The air time was donated by the station. But when the broadcast became popular, it was taken over by the Ministry of Forest. It was done "only for the money," Tamrakar criticized, "not from the heart."

Then, fortunately, the International Union for the Conservation of Nature (IUCN) in Switzerland offered to back her current programs. With the success of the shows, though, she is fearful that the government will again want to take over.

Eventually, Tamrakar would like to quit her state broadcasting job to devote all her time to environmental programs. Meanwhile, she has an uneasy working relationship with her government employers. "All the time" there are problems, she said. Although the current government is "a bit freer" than the last, she said, all her scripts must still be censored before airing.

Environmental journalists in rich countries have problems, too—ironically, they are mostly financial. The American newspaper *High Country News*, published in Paonia, Colorado, has battled money problems for many years to earn the nickname "the con-

Many Third World countries are rapidly developing their industries, creating scenes of striking contrasts. (Photograph © by Mark Edwards/Still Pictures)

science of the [U.S.] West." The biweekly newspaper's limited circulation of 8,000 belies its importance. According to its surveys, readers include most of the congressional delegations of the Western states. About 30 percent of its readers work for government agencies, and 18 percent are education professionals.

Bruce Babbitt, the environmentally-minded former governor of Arizona, said that the upstart newspaper was indispensable: "There is simply no other way to know what's going on, particularly as environmental controversies develop which have not yet reached the courts or the administrative process or Congress. It's required reading."

The paper, which editor Betsy Marston describes as "small and presumptuous," is known and highly regarded for its balanced reporting on environmental, economic, and cultural issues that affect the Western United States—mainly Colorado, Utah, Montana, Wyoming, and Idaho.

The small, full-time staff includes Marston, her husband and publisher Ed Marston, and a few unpaid interns. The paper relies for news on its network of 150 freelance correspondents. They contribute stories on controversial—and often intensely emotional—issues such as logging of ancient forests, the plight of Pacific salmon, the future of Yellowstone National Park, damage from cattle grazing and ecological threats from recreational development, and water projects in the arid West. Some of its articles have become major stories, picked up by *The New York Times* and other U.S. media.

Ed Marston, a former college physics professor, and Betsy Marston, an award-winning television producer, left New York City in 1974 to take a year off in the West. They stayed and have been running the paper since 1983. They edit the stories with an eye toward fairness. Betsy Marston, whom we met at the Society of Environmental Journalists' conference in Boulder, Colorado, said, "We don't tell the readers what to do. We assume that people are educated and they can connect issues. But of course we have a point of view," and that shows up in the selection of stories. "We don't like the label 'advocacy,' but we do have a beat—the environment."

"I don't believe in objectivity," she said, "but we try to be fair." That means including opposing points of view, whether from federal agencies, developers, or locals trying to preserve their way of life.

"While our role is to promote land and wildlife conservation," according to her husband, "we must recognize that people need to earn a living." In a series he did for the paper on "Reopening the Western Frontier," Marston wrote: "The environmental agenda of more wilderness, more wild rivers, less logging, less drilling, and less mining is well enough, so far as it goes. But a vision that sees only land and wildlife has the same weakness as a vision that sees only ore bodies and old-growth forests. A vision that does not recognize the small communities and rural human activities that accompany the land and wildlife has an enormous blindspot."

This balance has earned *High Country News* the trust and respect of the people whose actions it covers, as well as of its loyal readers, who once kicked in $30,000 in the late 1980s when the paper was in danger of folding. Donations and foundation grants now help stretch the budget. The paper's integrity also earned it a prestigious George Polk Award for environmental reporting, as well as a 1990 Global 500 award. "I really care about doing it right," Betsy Marston told us. "I don't see any point in doing it any other way."

Children watch a solar-powered television in the remote village of Azeel, Niger. (Photograph © by Mark Edwards/Still Pictures)

8

Image Makers

The effort to help people relate to their global habitat has been waged on many fronts. Among the most influential of Global 500 laureates are the television documentary producers and still photographers, who bring to viewers around the world powerful images of the natural world and its destruction by unnatural causes.

Jacques Cousteau, France's celebrated 1988 laureate and the dean of marine photography, introduced millions of television viewers around the globe to the beautiful and beleaguered world below the waterline. To capture his images, Cousteau and his crew had to pioneer undersea filming technology. And in doing so, the Frenchman established nature documentaries as stable fare on the burgeoning television medium in the post-World War II period.

A nature film series can cost millions of dollars and take years to complete. After David Attenborough, a 1987 Global 500 winner, made *The Living Planet* series for the BBC, publicity material proudly noted that he had traveled 240,000 kilometers and employed forty cameramen, who filmed in sixty-three countries from such extreme altitudes as 11,000 meters high in an aircraft and 2,500 meters below the ocean's surface in a deep-sea submersible carrier. The project, which took three-and-a-half years to plan, film, and edit, also transported crews and equipment by hot-air balloons, hang gliders, ocean-going canoes, all kinds of aircraft and motor vehicles, ski mobiles, sailing boats, motor boats, and donkeys.

Not all television producers can afford the high cost of an Attenborough-style production for worldwide distribution, but many producers have successfully produced less extravagant environmental shows. Global 500 winners Josef Velek (1989) of Czechoslovakia, Gabor Racz (1987) of Hungary, Uri Marinov (1989) of Israel, Jose Maussan Flota (1990) of Mexico, and Barbara Pyle and Robert Richter (1989) of the United States were each cited for their television work.

Joaquin Araujo, a Spaniard who won the Global 500 in 1991, demonstrates what can be done with a relatively restricted budget. He has produced roughly 200 television programs on nature, some of which have been shown outside Spain. In twenty-three years as an "environmental fighter," as he put it at the Stockholm award ceremony, he has had more than 400 journalistic pieces and fifteen books published, and finds time to plant 1,000 trees yearly. Television is just another arrow in his quiver.

Still photographers, who often work alone and with more limited budgets, are the image makers most apt to pursue a personal vision. Three of the world's best have been named to the Global 500: Americans Robert Glenn Ketchum and Jim Brandenburg, both selected in 1991, and Britain's Mark Edwards, a 1990 winner whose pictures illustrate many pages of this volume, including the cover. Although their medium is the same, each photographer has a unique way of sharing his vision of the world.

Robert Glenn Ketchum

Ketchum clearly identifies himself as an environmental activist. With absolute justification, he also calls himself an artist. A perfectionist, he works tirelessly to accent the nuances of color and background that make his nature pictures come alive.

Laureate Robert Redford (see page 99), after extolling Ketchum's pho-

Logging practices in Alaska threaten the Tongass, one of the world's largest nonequatorial rainforests. (Photograph © 1987 by Robert Glenn Ketchum)

tography, added, "Behind the exceptional work is a deeply committed and talented man." In a photographic book, *The Tongass: Alaska's Vanishing Rainforest*, Ketchum documented a U.S. environmental tragedy—the U.S. Forest Service's stewardship of its largest forest, the Tongass in southeast Alaska.

"Tongass is one of the largest nonequatorial rainforests in the world," Ketchum told us over lunch at the 1991 Stockholm awards ceremony. "Americans are quick to criticize countries like Brazil. But we cut down twice as many trees as Brazil. The Tongass is a public forest that is being quietly leased out by the government for timber extraction."

Ketchum found the whole issue of U.S. government land management "complex" but nevertheless "inexcusable." He has set about documenting what the various and overlapping land-management bureaucracies are doing—and what they should be doing.

Another book of Ketchum's photographs, *Overlooked in America*, has the look of an art book, replete with gorgeous pastoral scenes of the Ohio State's Cuyahoga Valley National Recreation Area (CVNRA). But the work, subtitled, *The Success and Failure of Federal Land Management*, is a lure to get Americans to read the unattractive facts about U.S. park management.

Ketchum's introduction tells readers that he is deeply disturbed by the federal management of the lands and the "complete lack of understanding and concern on the part of the public at large as to what 'federal lands' are." He explains that "approximately one-third of all land of the United States is owned and managed by the federal government."

Ketchum also writes, "I have attempted to create a new, more generic kind of photograph: an icon of the landscape, not a specific and documentary description." He wants readers to feel that the photographs they are viewing could be their "backyard," not some far-off place of no consequence to them. "Beauty is often superficial," he wrote, explaining that CVNRA waters are "too toxic to drink or swim in," but the pollution does not show up in the innocent pastoral scenes.

The text of *Overlooked in America* makes no attempt to identify the picture sites or subjects. Instead, the reader is fed, along with basic information, a disturbing story of official U.S. land mismanagement that bears no direct relationship to the photographs of CVNRA:

- Opposite a crisp and arresting photograph of CVNRA trees in fall is the observation that ". . . the Grand Canyon regularly has such bad air pollution that it obscures the view and, on some days, car emissions in Yosemite Valley generate smoglike conditions comparable to a good-sized city."
- Above a picture of autumn leaves, the text notes, "Less than 1 percent of the nation's original virgin forests are protected from logging, and virtually all the remaining groves are scheduled for elimination under current U.S. Forest Service and Bureau of Land Management plans."
- Opposite an inviting picture of a forest stream in winter, the text reads, "Seven of the ten most endangered rivers in America are on public lands."

"The collective intent of my work," Ketchum wrote, "has always been to encourage a universal appreciation of the planet's astounding life-forms rather than a site-specific visitation lust." *Overlooked in America,* then, is a persuasive trick on the reader to put over the point that the real deception is how U.S. lands are managed. "Environmental issues have become terribly complex and difficult to understand," Ketchum said. "People who care must use their imagination to get their concerns across."

Jim Brandenburg is more apt to let his pictures speak for themselves. As a contract photographer for *The National Geographic,* the United States' premier geographic magazine, he has traveled the world with his camera. A natural historian, Brandenburg has taken notable pictures of life in Manchuria, the rhino in South Africa, and shots of what pristine North America must have looked like before European colonization. In addition to magazine work, he has produced and filmed for television and taken photographs to illustrate books.

The outdoorsman long had an "obsession" to photograph wolves that he described as "95 percent romantic." Abroad and in his native state of Minnesota, the only continental U.S. state to have significant wolf packs, he had only fleeting glimpses of the wary animal. In twenty years, he was able to get only seven good shots, none of them up to his professional standards.

After assigning him to a North Pole story, the editors of *The National Geographic* finally agreed that Brandenburg could go to

Ellesmere Island to shoot a story on the white animals there, such as the Arctic fox, Peary caribou, hares, weasels, snowy owls, ptarmigans, polar bears, beluga whales and, most excitingly for him, wolves! The island, located at the northernmost point of Canada's Northwest Territories, was still unspoiled by man.

A portrait of Buster. (Photograph © by Jim Brandenburg. All rights reserved)

On being informed of his Ellesmere assignment, Brandenburg invited fellow Minnesotan, L. David Mech, a friend and noted wolf scientist, to join him. The Ellesmere site held two photographic advantages that Brandenburg never had before: the animals were unafraid of humans and they did not have many good places to hide. The two men quickly found the den of a pack and established a work base.

Brandenburg spent three summers photographing the wolf pack, first for *National Geographic Magazine* and then for a *National Geographic* television show. The wolves accepted the men, who returned the favor by giving the wolves such names as Buster, Left Shoulder, Lone Ranger, and Scruffy. Brandenburg concluded that the white wolves, which he described as "timid," "didn't show

(Photograph © by Jim Brandenburg)

aggression or fear because man had not lived on the island for 1,000 years." Wolves in other places, however, were constantly being hunted and had built up an innate fear of humans.

Brandenburg said that as time went on, he began to feel like a member of the pack in a never-never world. The fact remained, however, that he had to work much of the time under terrible and dangerous conditions, especially for a photographer who must deal instantaneously with sensitive equipment and fast action.

"I was only afraid of three things—bush pilots, the extreme cold, and polar bears," he said. "The bush pilots are good, but the flying is dangerous. The seventy-below temperature takes your breath away. We didn't carry any arms. Polar bears can have you any time they want to. But I savor the moments I spent on Ellesmere."

Of all the superb pictures he took, the most celebrated shot is a portrait of Buster, the Alfa Male, or leader, of the pack. In his stunning photographic book, *White Wolf*, he described how he got the picture. While he was fumbling with his camera settings in the freezing cold, "Buster trotted overs to a flat projection halfway up the iceburg, and from this makeshift throne he eyed me with a mixture of wariness and bemusement. A solitary shaft of light slanted sharply from the northern horizan, illuminating the wolf while leaving the surrounding iceburg in blue, muted shadow. It was the most exquisite composition nature had ever provided me."

The scene and lighting were perfect, but it was a long time before Brandenburg knew how the photographs, which had to be sent to *National Geographic* headquarters in Washington, D.C., for processing, came out. When the pictures and story of the wolf pack were finally published, they solidified his reputation as a great nature photographer.

White Wolf sold more than 75,000 copies. "I was greatly surprised by the sale," he admitted. "People must like wolves." In fairy tales and in legend, the wolf is demonized as an enemy of mankind. But Jim Brandenburg's photographs and television documentary permitted people to see the wolf as it really is, a resourceful animal surviving against all odds. "It is a great misconception," he said, "to think of the wolf as our enemy."

Unlike Ketchum's artistic landscape compositions and Brandenburg's more naturalistic shots, Mark Edwards' work highlights the dilemma of people around the world faced with environmental degradation. Since 1970, he has documented the growing global environmental crisis in more than fifty countries, and has become the unofficial photographer of the worldwide conservation movement.

Edwards's London library provides many of the images found in environmental publications around the world. He has photographed such diverse subjects as toxic waste pollution in Mexico City's slums, pollution and siltation of Italy's River Po, the effects of acid rain in Sweden, and deforestation in the tropics of Brazil.

Absolutely devoted to his craft, Edwards has a special sensitivity to Third World problems and people. In the *Global 500 Newsletter*, he described his thoughts while photographing Mexican children playing along some railroad tracks, near an open sewer behind a chemical refinery.

> The sun was going down, its light reflecting off the tracks, when a young woman came with her baby. It was only a few days old and she wanted to introduce him to the children. Even without the photographs you would always remember their expressions as they looked at the baby's face. To the outsider that child is part of an intractable problem—another addition to Mexico City's huge population. But these children had no conception of numbers. They had migrated from the land their parents had farmed when the soil blew away as one by one the trees were cut down. They had rebuilt their world along the railway tracks, and as I walked back to my comfortable hotel I really wondered what kind of a life they would lead.

"I don't want merely to show the planet in crisis," Edwards said. "I want to show how ordinary people respond to that crisis. It is the plight of the poor that should make us see the virtue of sustainable development."

9

The Voices of Nature

Stories, plays, folk tales, and the like have been used to educate, inform, distract, and delight since humans developed the capacity to communicate. Music, especially, has been an integral part of human cultures since the dawn of time. Because it speaks directly to the soul, it can convey messages across geographic, linguistic, and cultural boundaries.

Ully Sigar Rusady is a singer and songwriter who has channeled the power of music toward environmental protection. In her native Indonesia, she is known as the "Green Guitar." The Global 500 laureate is famed throughout her country and beyond for her songs about nature—its beauty, its importance, and its endangerment at the hands of human beings. In her clear soprano voice she sings of forests cut and burned, oceans fouled, air polluted, and mountains denuded. With a passion and purpose, she tries to convey through her music her love of the natural world.

My Earth, where is your joyous face
Of the beauty of the forests,
Of the green of your vales?
Are you reluctant to adorn yourself? Why?

My Earth, where is your majestic
symphony
Of songs of the wild animals,
Of sweet songs of your birds?
Are you reluctant to sing? Why?

—Ully Sigar Rusady from Bells, a song
Global 500 laureate

Ironically, we met Rusady in one of the fouled areas of the world—Indonesia's capital city of Jakarta, where automobiles clog the streets and pollution clouds the air.

"Music and nature cannot be separated," she began. "Music is knowledge, music is language, music is therapy." She has tried to spread this therapy far and wide: she has recorded several albums and her music is played on the radio and television. Some of her lyrics have been translated into other languages. One song, "Peace in the World," is now sung in seven languages. She keeps her lyrics simple so that one and all—young and old, scholars and villagers, native tribals and foreigners—can comprehend the message that the environment is at risk.

The natural environment has always been a part of Rusady's life. As a child growing up in a small West Javan village, her father used to take her into the forest, where she fell in love with its beauty. "Its beauty gives us spirit, gives us power to love," she said. On repeated trips into the forest, however, she noticed more and more trees cut down, leaving barren, eroding hills. "It wasn't beautiful anymore." Seeing firsthand the damage to one of her favorite spots, she asked herself, "What can I do about this?" The answer came in the form of music; at the age of ten, she wrote her first environmental song.

Rusady can more often be found wandering the forests and mountain ranges of Indonesia's 13,600 islands than in her office in the smoggy, congested capital. She feels much more at home hiking up mountains or trekking through the jungle in army surplus clothes, a kerchief restraining her long dark hair, her neck and wrists heavy with beads and bangles that she has picked up in her travels. Fortunately, her husband, who runs a computer shop in Jakarta, understands and supports her passion. Although he and their daughter stay at home, Rusady often takes her teenage son along.

It was on one such trip that she was "discovered" by the international development community. She was visiting the Dayak tribe in Borneo to teach them about environmental protection and conservation and, in turn, to learn about their use of music in traditional agricultural practices. A UNEP representative happened to be visiting the isolated village at the same time. He was transfixed by Rusady and her work, and nominated her for the Global 500 award.

For her body of work she was named to the Roll of Honor in 1987. "I was shocked," she said. "I'm only doing this because I love it. I'm not educated in the environment. I'm only a human being. I love music, I love nature, I love people."

Ully Sigar Rusady

But through her vision, she has brought all three elements together in a campaign to raise environmental awareness. In 1979 she started a music school—called Vidi Vici—for poor children who otherwise could not afford to study music (she, as a child, could not). Through the school, she coordinates plays and song contests with nature as the theme.

Soon after establishing the school she began enrolling many so-called "problem children" who were homeless, had family troubles, or had dropped out of school. She taught them for free, with the stipulation that they themselves become teachers or performers. The response to this program was so overwhelming that in 1985 she organized a foundation—the *Garuda Nusantara,* named after the country's national bird—to focus on these youths. The foundation's aim is to develop the talents of Indonesian youths who have been given up to the streets. Rusady instills in them confidence, competence, and a love for the environment by taking them out of the city to experience nature firsthand.

The children are divided into different activity groups. One goes to forest villages to carry out environmental projects, such as building irrigation channels. Another performs martial arts movements that evoke environmental images. A third sings environmental songs on the city streets. With boundless energy, Rusady teaches her charges discipline and gives them love. They return that love and respect, calling her *bunda,* Indonesian for "mother."

The path has not always been easy, Rusady admitted. Many of the children come from very troubled backgrounds and have been difficult to work with. Also, fundraising for the foundation has been challenging, and her message is not always well received. "They used to call me the 'misunderstood woman,' " she said of her compatriots. "They didn't understand me because they thought I was wasting time—why bother with the environment, with these children? Many people don't understand how to start protecting nature. I show them—go to nature, touch nature, and it will take you from there. It's a step-by-step process." Now that Rusady has received international recognition through the Global 500 award, people are slowly realizing the merit of her work.

After receiving the award, she proposed that UNEP sponsor an international song contest based on events similar to those she organized through her music school. The outcome was the "Regional Environment Song Festival—Asia Pacific," held in Bangkok during World Environment Day 1988. She then participated in a fundraising television campaign for the Women's Development Project in Oslo, Norway. She has also traveled to Beijing, Paris, Munich, New York, Nairobi, and Kathmandu, expanding her own horizons as well as those of people she touches with her songs.

Halfway around the world from Indonesia, another form of entertainment is being used to educate the public about the environment. Snake in the Grass Moving Theatre, a theatrical troupe in British Columbia that was named to the Global 500 list in 1990, uses drama to deliver its message. "The performing arts," the company's brochure explains, "are particularly flexible and offer enormous potential both as a means to raise awareness about environmental problems, and as adjuncts or 'back-up' to specific environmental projects."

In performances and dramatic "installations," the troupe weaves environmental themes into stories that also draw on mythology, technology, anthropology, and science fiction. *Ghosts in the Machine* is the nonprofit company's most environmentally oriented piece to date. It attacks the prevailing cultural paradigm that worships industrial and technological achievement by spotlighting the spiritual poverty and environmental destruction that ensue.

The troupe's writer, Paul Gibbons, who is trained in social anthropology as well as theater, writes the following in the play's program notes: "Is the blind trust, authority and faith we place in

Actors from Snake in the Grass Moving Theatre perform *Ghosts in the Machine*. (Photograph by Enrique Machon)

technology turning the means and manifestations of it into symbols and icons for worship and desire? Is the 'deification' or 'iconization' of technology separating us from our humanity, thereby threatening our own relevance and existence, or have we begun to turn the awesome potentials of technology into real human tools in order to establish a workable balance between 'nature' and our contemporary 'culture'?"

Ghosts in the Machine is peopled by "Dream Ghosts" and "Doppelgangers" that "are metaphors for different aspects of the contemporary human psyche. The Doppelgangers are attached to the miraculous and/or devastating possibilities of technology—the excitement and pace of main-stream Western culture. The Dream Ghosts, on the other hand, are attached to the ancient forces and rhythms of the Earth itself." Each of the four Dream Ghosts is dressed in monochrome—one black, one white, one red, one yellow. "They symbolize not only elemental earth forces and the four directions, but also the different races."

Not all the troupe's plays put environment at the forefront. Often, the message is subtly woven in. For example, the troupe's publicity brochure says *Through the Black Hole* and *In the Photon Zone* "use a science fiction format to trace connections between ancient metaphysical systems and recent developments in physics and biology, and, above all remind us of the delicate ecological balance between all living organisms."

Similarly, performances given as part of a children's education program at the University of British Columbia Museum of Anthropology dramatize mythologies, especially those of the native people of the northwest coast—"people who were able to live in vital harmony with the environment until the arrival of the Europeans. Through their mythologies we learn too about the respect and reverence these people have for the natural world—the source of all our riches."

By not advertising all the group's works as "being specifically 'environmental'," it hopes "access is gained to a wide variety of audiences, and environmental 'messages' can be introduced to people who might otherwise be unreceptive."

The company has performed in theaters, museums, planetariums, parks, prisons, parades, schools, festivals, hospitals, conferences, and community environments. The troupe's message can be universally understood, for its works use language sparingly. To convey its messages the actors rely mostly on color, costume, music, movement, and huge, fantastic masks.

We saw one of the costumes at the 1990 award ceremony in Mexico City, where we met Paul Gibbons and the company's Co-Artistic Director, Tsuneko Kokubo. Kokubo attended the many events dressed in grey and black rags, with a white-painted face, and did not speak a word. Her dramatic attire and continuing silence sparked the curiosity of the other awardees, but she refused to answer any questions throughout the several days leading up to the awards ceremony. Only then did she finally give up her character as she and Gibbons explained about Snake in the Grass and its work.

Entertainers can use their talents offstage as well. Robert Redford, the American actor, director, and producer is renowned for his blond hair, blue eyes, and starring roles in movies such as *Butch Cassidy and the Sundance Kid*, *Jeremiah Johnson*, *Out of Africa*, *The Great Gatsby*, *The Natural*, and *The Candidate*. But while Hollywood is his full-time job, the environment comes in a very close second.

Redford began supporting environmental causes long before they became fashionable. As he writes in the introduction to *Save the Earth*, a collection of writings on the environment by well-known environmental supporters around the world, compiled by Global 500 laureate Jonathon Porritt: "My own involvement started before I knew it, growing up in Los Angeles. It was a beautiful place then. I watched as the green, open spaces turned into concrete malls and freeways and the clean air turned into smog alerts. I watched as unbridled development became the order of the day. Oil drills appeared off the beaches, along with oil spills in the water and hunks of tar on the sand. The smell of orange blossoms turned into exhaust fumes. It seemed like my home was eroding beneath my feet. I felt my roots being pulled out from under me. I began to take it personally."

In 1974 he lobbied for the Clean Air Act, and in 1975 was an active and highly visible opponent of a coal-fired power plant proposed for an area bordered by five national parks in his adoptive home state of Utah. The power plant was never built, but Redford's involvement in the campaign did nothing for relations with his neighbors. He was hung in effigy in a nearby town. Long-time locals, many of whom make a living off the land by ranching, mining, logging, and farming, resented the intrusion by this Hollywood superstar whose nature conservation ethics seemed to threaten their livelihoods.

"It got pretty hairy . . . ," Redford said, "I began to think that my speaking out so much as an individual had a dubious effect, that maybe a more effective use of my time and energy would be to create an organization with experts who could actually do something about the environment."

This line of thought led to his founding of the Institute for Resource Management (IRM) in 1983 as a means of bringing industrial and environmental leaders together face-to-face, through thematic conferences, to discuss ecological problems and cooperate on solutions.

As a result of the first conference, on the future of the electric utility industry, industry representatives adopted a resolution to promote energy conservation, not just consumption. Other conferences have focused on the subjects of energy exploration on Indian tribal lands, oil drilling in the Bering Sea, and logging practices in U.S. national forests. The IRM has also sponsored a series of workshops in Denver, Phoenix, Sacramento, and New York City on the quality of urban air.

The IRM's most publicized event was the "Greenhouse Glasnost Conference" in 1989. The conference grew out of an agreement between the IRM and the Soviet Academy of Sciences, signed during a trip Redford made to the Soviet Union the previous year. The agreement promised cooperation in research, public education, and policy development on issues related to the greenhouse effect. The conference, which was attended by scientists, policymakers, industry leaders, and artists from both countries, resulted in letters to both U.S. President George Bush and Soviet President Mikhail Gorbachev outlining specific recommendations to reduce global warming.

The meeting drew hordes of media representatives as well as political and environmental heavyweights to Redford's home and headquarters in Sundance, Utah. They came not only for the issues and the beautiful Utah vistas, but to see the star himself. "One of the advantages of being known," Redford said, "is you can command access to the experts."

Critics point out that despite the assembled experts and good intentions, IRM has no political clout. They also point out that Redford's support of environmental causes that go against big business is ironic, as he himself is a developer—his Sundance spread includes the Sundance Ski Resort, which he founded and still operates.

It is true that the institute has no political leverage. But it does raise public awareness of environmental issues and fosters cooperation between environmental and industrial leaders who are often diametrically opposed. While many in the environmental movement eschew any dialogue with industry, Redford argues that industry is here to stay and must be included in discussions if any progress is to be made.

Redford defends his development of a ski resort by contending that the land would not have been treated so kindly if bought by someone else. He says he has developed only 27 of his 2,000 hectares and has planted organic gardens and trees and established his own recycling stations. By building on the land in his own limited and thoughtful fashion, he claims he is saving it from a worse fate.

Although some of the criticism may be warranted, Redford is considered by many in the environmental field to be a "serious player" who has advanced public awareness and support for both national and global environmental issues. He was named to the Global 500 Roll of Honor in 1987 for his achievements. Although he left the IRM in 1991 to pursue other projects, he is not about to give up on the cause.

His film company, Sundance Films, produced a short film on solar energy, which was nominated for an Academy Award, and a documentary on Yosemite National Park, called *Yosemite: The Fate of Heaven*. Redford himself sits on the boards of Friends of the Earth USA, the Environmental Defense Fund, and the Natural Resources Defense Council.

In all his activities, his tactic is to educate ordinary people about the issues with the belief that once informed, they will act. "We can't rely on politics, we can't rely on government or the administration," he said. "I honestly think it's going to come from . . . people doing things on a local level. I'm a little old-fashioned and I really do believe in the power of the people. . . . The best thing we can do about the environment is to educate people. Then have enough faith in the people that once they understand, they're going to be mad enough, frustrated enough, impatient enough to do something about it."

Another American star who has lent her support to an environmental cause is actress Christine Hicks. Though not nearly as big a name as Redford, Hicks has gained her share of fame through her role as a marine biologist in the film *Star Trek IV: The Voyage Home,* seen by millions of people around the world since it opened in the United States in November 1986.

In this particular Star Trek release, the biologist played by Hicks transports a male and female humpback whale into the future, saving the species from extinction. To research her role, Hicks talked to marine biologists, read numerous books on whales, and watched a *National Geographic* documentary on the huge mammals.

Her experience with the film motivated her to take part in real-life whale conservation activities. "You wake up one morning and your conscience just goes ding-a-ling," she explained. She has been interviewed extensively in the Connecticut media because of her close work with the Cetacean Society International, a nongovernmental organization based in the coastal state that is very active in the global whale conservation movement. Since her awakening to the movement, Hicks has become a successful public fundraiser for all marine mammals through public appearances, interviews, and seminars. Like Redford, she has found that as a big-screen star, "You have contact with more powerful phones."

10

The Greening of Capitalism

> Industry extracts materials from the natural resource base and inserts both products and pollution into the human environment. It has the power to enhance or degrade the environment.
>
> —*World Commission on Environment and Development Global 500 laureate*

Europe and North America "conquered" their natural surroundings to extract the lifeblood of an industrial society, setting the standard for economic development throughout the world. But the industrial model they set up seems ecologically unsustainable on a global basis. As industrialization spreads throughout the world, where will the balance fall? Enhancement or degradation? And how can corporations of the industrialized world be policed—and police themselves—to achieve sustainable development? John Elkington, a British Global 500 laureate who specializes in corporate responsibility, has dealt extensively with these issues.

His walk-up office is located in a nondescript section of London. A bicycle leans against a whitewashed wall that is decorated by a green globe on an apple stem. The bare wood floor and functional furniture create a down-to-earth atmosphere. A quintessential "green," Elkington is faithful to his surroundings.

Elkington and Julia Hailes were jointly named to the Global 500 list in 1989 for writing *The Green Consumer Guide*, a number-one bestseller in the United Kingdom. The book gives the average shopper a practical rundown on which products are ecologically sound and which are not. Elkington has coauthored two other books, *The Green Business Guide* and *The Green Capitalists*, and founded a company, SustainAbility Ltd., which counsels corporations on environmental communications and policy.

In *The Green Consumer Guide*, he emphasizes that "our consumer choices affect the environment. Yet most of us are unaware of the positive influence we can exert through our spending power." The outpouring of help in the writing of the book from concerned citizens, and the subsequent sales of more than one million copies, demonstrated that an influential mass of ecologically minded buyers was, in fact, forming.

Elkington also points out that "we are witnessing the birth of corporate environmentalism." Not only are increasing regulations and consumer awareness forcing ecological responsibility, but people who grew up in the 1960s, a decade of radical change, are coming to positions of real power in the boardrooms of business.

One of the most extreme examples of a sixties-type making it big in business is Anita Roddick, a 1989 Global 500 laureate. The onetime hippie founded the highly successful chain of Body Shop cosmetic stores in the United Kingdom. Starting in 1976 with medical urine-sample bottles for cosmetic containers in a hole-in-the-wall shop between two Brighton morticians, the Body Shop quickly grew into an international enterprise worth $600 million.

Rather than the fatuous glamour and romance peddled by the traditional multi-billion-dollar cosmetic firms, The Body Shop promotes no "idealised notions of beauty," pushes natural products, promises no animal testing of its products, and disseminates a philosophy about "profits and principles" going hand-in-hand.

The Body Shop's concern for the environment is also used as a selling point for the products. The company began printing advertising materials on recyclable paper long before it was fashionable, uses "minimal packaging," and holds "regular internal environmental audits" to ensure that the company conserves resources and keeps manufacturing "as clean as possible."

Finding natural products from the Third World was made an article of faith, especially in the context of human rights. From the beginning, Roddick was dedicated to finding raw materials in the rainforest. By purchasing renewable forest products such as oils, nuts, and plant extracts from indigenous tribes, she hopes to create income that will allow them to survive on their own terms, maintaining harmony with the natural environment that sustains them. "The Body Shop is more than a cosmetic company," claims Roddick. "We are an emissary for social change."

The unconventional executive, whose green philosophy and persona dominate The Body Shop's public image and internal management, gains attention through extensive travel in her ongoing search for raw materials and natural cosmetic recipes. On her return from Nepal, her published diary related her delight in meeting a member of the *aguri*, the "left hand sect which believes in defying conventional morality by drinking human blood, eating feces and making love to corpses. This may seem abhorrent, but what is extreme and odd to us they consider natural."

Not everyone praises Roddick's campaign to support traditional Third World lifestyles. Critic Amber Kennedy, writing for *The World Paper*, characterized it as "patronizing" and "exploitative" because "it doesn't take into account the material aspirations of developing countries, preferring rather that they remain as they are."

Opponents may challenge Roddick's philosophy, but it is hard to gainsay her business acumen. The Body Shop tapped a latent feeling that unrestrained and unthinking consumerism was ecologically destructive and ethically wrong. Roddick's success demonstrates that profits can go hand in hand with "green" principles.

A retailer can be "green" in a way that heavy industry cannot. Extractive industries in particular are in constant conflict with environmentalists, especially purists who believe that metals should stay in the ground. The aluminum industry is a perfect example of this conflict, and two Global 500-winning companies provide examples of how industry can mitigate ore extraction's destructive impact on the Earth.

The German company Hoogovens Aluminium Huettenwerk GmbH, a 1991 winner, is a smelter plant cited in the award booklet as "a fine example of how industry and nature can co-exist." The plant is set on ninety-two hectares, of which eighty have been turned into a nature reserve. The company has planted native trees and bushes and constructed two large ponds to attract various

Left, Alcoa of Australia employees "plant" on a rehabilitated bauxite minesite in Western Australia. It is hoped that birds will perch on the branches and that seed in their droppings will germinate. This is one of a number of innovative ideas being tested by the Alcoa Environmental group. **Above,** employees conduct a meter-by-meter survey of another former minesite one year after seeding to check on germination of species. **Below,** seedlings are grown for use in these projects; however, more and more reforestation is being done using seeds applied directly at the site. (Photographs © Mark Edwards/Still Pictures)

wildlife to the reserve. Another twenty hectares have been set aside as forest.

The aluminum company Alcoa of Australia, a 1989 winner, is also carrying out a reforestation program but on land from which it has extracted bauxite. The process leaves gaping holes in the ground and also requires a great amount of energy—a further drain on the environment—to convert the bauxite into alumina and alumina into aluminum.

Alcoa's potentially damaging operation is further exposed to public scrutiny because it operates in an ecologically unique recreational area, the Jarrah Forest, which lies near Perth and other populous cities. One of the few remaining major forested areas in Western Australia, it is also a focus of conservationists.

The Jarrah Forest, much of which is designated as a national park, is also a major source of the region's water supply and provides raw material for the nation's timber industry. The jarrah tree, which in the area's nutrient-poor soil takes sixty to seventy years to mature to a millable log, is celebrated as a beautifully grained, red-hued hardwood that makes exquisite furniture.

The stakes that bauxite holds for the company, and the country's economy, are very high. Australia has roughly 20 percent of the world's known bauxite reserves and produces nearly 40 percent of the world's mined bauxite. But continued access to the reserves, in the words of Alcoa's Environmental Manager, Graham C. Slessar, "ultimately depends on community acceptance of the mining operation, and this can only be maintained if the operations are conducted in a socially and environmentally responsible manner."

Rather than fight a rearguard action against public concerns, Alcoa has sought to establish itself as an environmental leader, assigning a staff of thirty to deal with ecological issues. Public tours allow outsiders to view the operations for themselves, and Alcoa undergoes independently assessed monitoring and invites examination by touting its own environmental programs as a showcase. For

> *Unfortunately, too many companies assume that exploitation of the environment for dumping waste or acquiring raw materials is essential to their success, much as factory owners early in the Industrial Revolution thought their survival depended on the exploitation of child labor.*
>
> ***—Lester Brown***
> ***Global 500 laureate***

instance, the company won major recognition as the outright winner of the 1987 Greening of Australia Award for supporting tree planting outside of its minesites.

Alcoa of Australia received the Global 500 award for its program to reforest excavated minesites. The jarrah tree, which is the focus of this effort, grows on the 1.4 million hectares of the harsh Darling Range where bauxite is found. While only an estimated 3 or 4 percent of the forest contains the ore, Brian Wills-Johnson, Alcoa's public relations manager and a main mover of its environmental program, affirmed that "every hectare of forest is precious for a number of reasons and must be carefully rehabilitated after mining."

In more than two decades of operations, Alcoa claims it has cleared less than 0.5 percent of the Jarrah Forest for mining and infrastructure. At a spot where bauxite is to be extracted, topsoil is collected and transported to another minesite that is being rehabilitated. Stockpiling is avoided whenever possible to maintain the fresh topsoil's maximum nutritional value.

Alcoa's nurseries experiment with seedlings that best suit the area's infertile soil, and company scientists take precautions to curb the spread of fungus that attacks jarrah trees. The scientists have demonstrated that the jarrah and most of the understory trees can be reestablished at mine locations. As a result of the company's work, its spokesman can boast that "Alcoa is recognized internationally as a leader in minesite rehabilitation."

In addition, Alcoa has spent money and time—more than a decade—converting some of its early, abandoned minesites into wetlands. With the help of outside scientists, the company has created an area that now hosts a wide variety of birds.

"We are not perfect," Graham Slessar remarked at the time of the Global 500 award, "and the UNEP award is not for perfection. In fifty years time, when we see the outcomes we now predict for the nature rehabilitation, we might be able to claim that."

After Alcoa of Australia was added to the Global 500 list, some of the other Australian laureates objected. Christine Milne, a Green Independent member of the Parliament of Tasmania and a 1990 laureate, wrote us to say she did not want to be part of this book, as it was funded in part by Alcoa of Australia, and she thinks their practices are deplorable.

But others are aware of the industrial realities in modern life. Mark Edwards, environmental photographer and also a 1990 laureate (see page 90), wrote about one of his picture-taking trips: "I am writing this article while on a Boeing 747. All the aluminum in the plane was made from bauxite mined by Alcoa in the Darling Range." His curiosity was aroused by the criticism of Alcoa's award, and he had just visited the company's mining sites. "After five months of photographing the problems around the world," he wrote, "it was exciting to be able to see such a well-managed and successful reforestation program. Hopefully it will inspire other mining companies to develop similar programs."

11

Quixotic Quests

While the pursuits of many of the Global 500 laureates are easy to categorize, a few of the winners seem more intent on chasing personal dreams than following strict environmental blueprints.

Bu Eroh, for instance, is an extraordinary woman by anyone's measure. At the age of forty-seven, this spirited peasant woman set out singlehandedly to change her world.

Her village compound of Pasir Kadu, set on an Indonesian mountainside only a few hours by car and foot from the town of Bandung, is close to the amenities of the modern world. But the compound still lacks electricity, and until 1987 the villagers did not even have a water supply. Women were forced to walk from one to five kilometers to fetch water for cooking, cleaning, and drinking.

In the dry season, no crops would grow. During the annual rains, the villagers could cultivate one harvest of cassava, the starchy rootstock that is a food staple throughout the tropics. The crop produced an average annual cash income of slightly more than five dollars. To supplement this meager amount, women would often go to the forest to hunt for mushrooms they could sell. The people survived, but life was hard work.

One day while Eroh was hunting mushrooms far from her compound, she came across a stream in the forest, and an idea began to take shape in her mind. Keeping quiet about her plans, she set to work. She borrowed $213 from the village's black market bank and used the funds to buy twenty chisels, twenty-five rock hammers, and forty meters of rope made from tree roots.

On her own, she began the task of constructing a 4.5-kilometer channel to carry water to her village from the stream. The work was not only difficult but dangerous. The first meters of the channel had to be chiseled out of a steep cliff about twenty-five meters high. Eroh would tie one end of the root rope around her waist and anchor the other end to a tree at the top of the cliff. Often she would work suspended seventeen meters off the ground. A fall could mean serious injury. And, with the village a three-hour walk away, there would be no one nearby to rescue her.

But she took the risk of working alone because the risk of ridicule was greater; if she involved other people right away and the far-fetched project failed, she would have to live down the laughter for the rest of her life.

So, while her husband thought she was out collecting mushrooms, she made slow but steady progress on the channel, carving out about one-and-a-half meters each day. Having attended the village school only until she was about nine years old, the poorly educated woman had to guess the proper incline for the channel to allow the water to flow all the way to the compound. She just carved where she felt it was right.

Finally, after forty-five days and forty-seven meters worth of solitary labor, she went to the village leader and told him of her work. He laughed in disbelief, as did her neighbors. They called her a madwoman for taking on this impossible task. But when the leader came to see the project first-hand he saw the possibility of success and dispatched nineteen village men to help out. Twice a week the band would go to the forest, using the chisels and hammers Eroh had bought with great optimism early on.

The men, however, would not venture onto the face of the rock, leaving this risky task to Eroh. And after eight days of work, nine of the men quit altogether, preferring to work for their own families rather than on a chancy community project.

Eroh and her remaining team worked on, and in March 1987, two-and-a-half years from her first cut into the rock, the channel was completed. About half of it courses across the cliff, and the rest is dug out of the ground. It measures one meter wide and twenty-five centimeters deep.

Because of the channel the compound is a different place. Ponds are stocked with fish that provide another source of food. Open-pit latrines built over the ponds improve sanitation and also allow fertilization of plankton that help feed the fish. Women need walk only five meters for fresh water. Bright green rice terraces cover the nearby hillsides. The farmers can get three rice crops a year instead of the one cassava harvest, allowing families to bring in more than $500 yearly.

Overall, the quality of life is much improved for Eroh's family, the more than 400 families in her compound, and another 800 families that live along the channel and in neighboring compounds.

And Eroh is a local celebrity. After the successful completion of the channel, the village leader passed word of her feat to the regional authorities, who passed it up to national figures, and in 1988 she received an award from the Indonesian government. This brought her to the attention of UNEP, and in 1989, at the age of fifty-one, Eroh was named to the Global 500 Honor Roll.

Fascinated by her story, we were able, with the generous help of some local contacts, to meet up with her in Pasir Kadu. On the eight-kilometer dirt trail from the road's end to her home, people waved to her, called her name, or just smiled and nodded in her direction.

Sitting cross-legged around the floor of her straw-mat home, resting after our steep trek, she smiled shyly, wondering what it was these strangers wanted to know. After seeing that everyone had a cup of warm tea, Eroh lit a cigarette and answered questions put to her through an interpreter.

Though the Global 500 certificate—actually a photocopy of it, as a local authority has kept the original—is framed on her wall along with other awards, she says frankly that the honor "has made no difference" in her life because it did not come with any money. She has been recognized in her community and has no plans to leave her village to work in the wider world.

After winning the award, she took on the job of compound leader—the first woman ever to do so. In this role she organizes work and social activities, advises on problems, and mediates disputes among the families in her compound. She also took over command of a team of workmen repairing and improving the path to Tasik, the town at the end of the nearest road.

Now, instead of calling her a "madwoman," her neighbors jokingly refer to her as a "tomboy" for her work on the channel, her leadership position, and her smoking—all highly unusual for

Bu Eroh as compound leader helps organize projects to improve her village in Pasir Kadu, Indonesia. (Photograph by Elizabeth Lee)

women in this rural, patriarchal part of the world. But the title carries no ridicule, only respect.

Eroh's completion of the water channel is a true success story, although some would argue that the diversion of water can have many negative consequences on the existing ecosystem. So even though she may not slip easily into a category of environmental achievement, Eroh has, against great odds, inarguably improved life for the people in her small corner of the world.

Tom Muller is another one-of-a-kind winner. But unlike Bu Eroh's heroic campaign to bring water to her small rural village, Muller's quest in Zimbabwe is national in scope. The 1988 Global 500 winner strives to build an enduring botanical garden in Harare, the country's capital, that will show his compatriots the beauty and worth of their natural surroundings.

Muller was recognized for replicating his country's major ecosystems, a project he painstakingly worked on since he was appointed as the garden's curator in 1962. When we met the Swiss-born botanist at the garden in 1991, he was racing against the deadline of his imminent retirement at age sixty-five.

Muller's project is well-advanced and most impressive. But two related doubts cloud its future. Firstly, will Muller, upon retirement, leave in place a staff capable of carrying on the work? And will the developing African nation find the botanical garden deserving of further financing in light of varied social problems?

Muller's unbending perfectionism, an ingredient needed to build the park, mitigated against both the training of a staff to carry on after he departs and establishing the importance of the project in the minds of private donors and key government officials.

Muller is not the easiest man to contact. We wrote him prior to our visit to Zimbabwe, but got no response. Upon our arrival there we phoned his office, still unable to reach him. So one Sunday we took a taxi to his research center at the sixty-eight-hectare National Botanical Garden on the outskirts of the city. We gently threw pebbles against a lit window, and finally our target emerged, smiling.

The transplanted Swiss walked us through the great garden. Even though we were not familiar with Zimbabwe's flora, we recognized that we were moving from one distinct habitat to another. The nation's major ecosystems—evergreen rainforest, high altitude forests, savanna woodland, lowland tree savanna, grassland riverine, and lake vegetation—are replicated in distinct clusters that are set off by well-kept grass.

Zimbabweans were picnicking, playing with their children, walking around the park, and lying on the grass. But Harare's "Garden of Eden" is more than a well-manicured park. The task of replicating several ecosystems in one area, Muller explained, is exacting, time-consuming, and scientifically challenging, especially on a very limited budget.

Zimbabwe, in common with most nations, has various—and often dramatically distinct—ecosystems based on four major soil categories, different altitudes and average temperatures, and regions of greatly differing amounts and periods of rainfall.

Muller, a man of firm convictions, and his small staff had to make sure that plantings were in proper sequences, allowing the canopy trees to take hold before understory species, a shrub layer, and ground cover were started. At the outset, expeditions were sent out to obtain proper seeds and seedlings for the botanical garden.

Water management can create microclimates needed in certain cases, with irrigation replicating rainforest conditions and water sprays increasing humidity. But recreating arid conditions can be accomplished only by a heavy investment in a greenhouse system, something that the botanical garden cannot afford. On top of all that, there is the occasional problem of frost.

In addition to Zimbabwean flora, Muller has laid out a section for exotic trees from around the world, particularly from other African nations. Some of the trees carry great value on the international market, and from time to time knowing thieves will steal the more precious ones.

The total effect of the plantings is a manifest success. "Apart from a few notable instances," Muller said, "varied forest species grow well here with careful attention." Out of Zimbabwe's estimated 780 indigenous species of trees, roughly 650 are found in the park. Of the nation's 1,200 woody plant species, about 1,000 have been successfully planted here. The failure rate of trying to introduce new species is estimated at less than 10 percent.

The energetic white-haired "gardener," as he calls himself, argues that "the garden is not just a collection of plants, it is a well thought out plan. If you make it aesthetically pleasing, people will be motivated to learn about plant species."

People may be motivated to learn, but there is virtually no budget for making information available to the public. The National Herbarium, situated on the grounds, has more than 250,000 plant specimens, but they are for scientific study only. It is Muller's dream—and the fond hope of knowledgeable observers—that the botanical garden will one day have a greenhouse, an interpretive center, horticultural displays, and a larger staff, and be able to provide educational materials and informed guides.

"I would like to display the whole spectrum of subtropical plants," Muller said. "If it comes off, we will have a greenhouse like you have never seen." But the impolitic Swiss is not one to sweet-talk Zimbabwean officials or the strapped private sector into providing necessary funds. A local magazine notes that "the running financial vote from Government is sufficient only for maintenance purposes and development depends on availability of private funds."

Because of Muller's imminent retirement, a Zimbabwean was trained to replace him but did not meet his standards and was removed. The dedicated botanist and gardener will leave, then, without having secured his lifelong project. Without proper funding and dedicated leadership, Harare's "Garden of Eden" could at best remain a lovely park whose remarkable plantings are only fully understood by the cognoscente. At worst, it could go to seed.

Whatever the case, Muller finds some satisfaction in having at least come this far. "What happens after I retire?" he asked rhetorically. "I can say I played the game nicely."

12

Magic Eyes

Many Global 500 laureates are average citizens who became increasingly distressed by the environmental degradation engulfing their world. Some, like Lily Venizelos (see page 6), reacted by fixing on one problem, in her case the Mediterranean loggerhead turtle's threatened extinction. Others have struck out to clean up the whole mess.

Chodchoy Sophonpanich decided to clean up her native Thailand, long considered one of Asia's biggest environmental messes. "It all started with my children," the elegant woman in her late forties told us as we sat in her fifteenth floor office overlooking polluted Bangkok. "I was trying to teach them to look after public areas. They kept asking me why. Nobody else was doing it. What was the use of teaching four kids to do the right thing when they were going to grow up with sixty million people doing the wrong thing?

"Thai people are very clean. We wash our clothes every day and we keep our houses clean. But we have never been taught to take care of our public areas. There is no word in Thai for 'environment'—the concept is abstract."

When she started to look into what could be done, "Everybody thought I was mad." Since even her educated contemporaries did not understand the problem, she decided "to brainwash a new generation of kids through advertising means."

A successful businesswoman with experience in marketing, Sophonpanich started her campaign in 1983 by coordinating private organizations that were already taking antipollution action and enrolling new environmental activists into what became the Thai Environmental and Community Development Association (TECDA). A three-point agenda was agreed upon: persuade the public to stop littering and to throw their trash in garbage bins; clean up existing rubbish in public places; and inculcate children with a sense of responsibility about keeping Thailand clean.

The logo of the campaign, a disembodied pair of black and white eyes set in a bright green circle, lent the project its name, "Magic Eyes." In Thai culture, Sophonpanich explained, "everyone is afraid of ghosts—and the eyes remind them of ghosts." The eyes became a "gentle remonstrance" against litter. Soon the Magic Eyes logo was seen all over Bangkok on television, newspapers, magazines, T-shirts, stickers, badges, teaching kits, and billboards. A radio jingle warned:

Ah, ah, don't litter!
Magic Eyes see you.

At the outset, a fifteen-second television commercial was aimed at children. It was so successful that Sophonpanich thought it would do the trick. "We didn't realize," she recalled, "that we were going to have to do so much more. Okay, we don't litter, but where do we find garbage bins? So we had to supply bins."

Through the Magic Eyes campaign, TECDA discovered that teachers wanted help instructing kids on environmental responsibility; communities wanted local programs and garbage bins; and citizens wanted help planting trees. "We went the way people wanted us to go," Sophonpanich said. "Need propels us."

The responsive campaign has reached its outer limits on the overwhelming problem of clean water for Bangkok. The capital has no proper waterborne sewage system and only a limited system of septic tanks. Houses as well as industries pour their waste into the canals. The result is a citywide open sewer. Many Thais must drink directly from the polluted water. Sanitary problems are compounded by seasonal flooding.

Despite the cost and complexity of the water problem, Sophonpanich noted, "We still have to help people who believe in us. We are now trying to find cheap, individual sewage treatment units to put in houses. We cannot wait for the city to take five years to build a municipal system, even if it decides to start now." TECDA

Every year Marevivo hosts the *Festa del Mare* (Sea Day), and participants nationwide help clean up the beaches of Italy. (Photograph © by Fotoattualita'di attilio Castantini)

is also urging industry to clean up after itself.

In common with many citizens' campaigns, TECDA discovered that preventing pollution can be more effective than cleaning it up. The organization stresses such conservation measures as turning off the tap while brushing one's teeth, using fewer disposable products, and recycling and reusing as many items as possible.

More than 100,000 citizens—school children, teachers, market vendors, housewives, private company employees, and community residents—have actively participated in TECDA's activities. Looking back on her success, Sophonpanich credits her 1987 Global 500 award with giving her a needed boost. Longtime environmentalists, she feels, were suspicious of her work because "she was so successful so fast" and, as the daughter of an important Bangkok banker, she was a "personality" in Thailand. "They forgot that I always was a businesswoman. What I am doing is not charity work, it is business. The 'bottom line' is not how much money we are making, but how well our 'product' sells. And our supporters are the 'shareholders.' "

TECDA has a Global 500 counterpart in Italy in Marevivo, an organization of citizens out to clean up the coastal water of the Mediterranean. The group grew out of twenty-six socialites' shared love of the sea. They met regularly at Capri, the celebrated resort island near the entrance to the Bay of Naples. In common with many coastal inhabitants and vacationers at the time, the water enthusiasts lamented the pollution of their playground.

Projected into the Mediterranean, the peninsula of Italy is dotted with 537 coastal cities of 10,000 people or more, who are a major source of pollution. So are the roughly 100 million people a year who use the Mediterranean Basin for recreation. Also, cargo boats and tankers spill oil into its waters and industry pours its waste into the sea.

To combat the increasing pollution, the Capri activists formed an independent, nonprofit organization that is financed almost exclusively by its membership. We visited the group's Rome headquarters, appropriately located on a houseboat on the Tiber River, where we spoke with Marevivo's director, Carmen Di Penta, about the association's campaign.

Marevivo's 30,000 members are "asked to roll up their sleeves and go to work, not to wait for the government to act," Di Penta told us. The association's emblematic campaign, she explained, is saving the *Posidonia oceanica,* "a plant of vital importance to the marine environment." The plant, which grows on the sea floor and deters erosion, is a vital part of the marine food chain and produces much-needed oxygen through photosynthesis. "The Mediterranean sea will die without oxygen," Di Penta added.

Marevivo also supports a variety of educational programs for the young, including one in which biologists show children the dynamics of marine life. "Education of children is most important," Di Penta said. "Once they are adults, it is very difficult to educate them."

On the first Sunday of every July, the association organizes a nationwide *Festa del Mare* (Sea Day). Demanding "concrete results," Marevivo sponsors a cleanup of beaches. Participants in the heavily publicized event pick up tons of litter, particularly plastics, from the waterfronts. Beach teams send in pictures and descriptions of their efforts to Marevivo. The best entries receive the honorary "Golden Dolphin Award."

Di Penta describes the association as apolitical, but the upper-class leadership has undoubted clout in all walks of Italian life. As an environmental lobby, it has "undertaken battles and campaigns" for sea reserves; the abolishment of the fishing industry's destructive drift nets; and tighter laws against the use of plastic bags and the dumping of pollutants into the sea. The group has also been asked by the European Economic Community to monitor the Italian coastline.

From a casual group of twenty-six vacationers in Capri, Marevivo in seven years has become a nationwide grassroots enviromental movement. Its success is not only a tribute to the power and competence of its founders, it indicates the dissatisfaction of many average Italians with the quality of their surroundings. "The decisive contribution for saving the Mediterranean," Di Penta said, "will come from [the] conscience and voice of the people."

In Mauritius, another nation surrounded by water, the *Fleurir Maurice* (Flower Mauritius) movement started in great measure as a reaction to the dirty, polluting sugar mills that covered the island. Begun at the time of the small nation's independence in 1968, the movement recognized not only that the people were living in unnecessarily squalid circumstances, but that cleaning up the island was the only way to continue attracting the tourists essential for its economic survival.

The *Fleurir Maurice* movement is a product of many cultures blended on this cluster of tiny islands. Located in the Indian Ocean approximately 1,800 kilometers off the Kenyan port of Mombasa, Mauritius was colonized in succession by the Dutch, French, and English.

"When we started, people just laughed," explained Chandranee K. Bhuckory, who accepted the Global 500 for *Fleurir Maurice* at the 1991 awards ceremony in Stockholm. "When we started, nobody used the word 'environment.' "

The movement has put special stress on engaging young people in cleanup and beautification efforts. Colorful posters are issued in French, bearing the slogan: "*Fleurir Maurice*—A clean country shines like a smile."

"We aim to convince all people that they shouldn't destroy the environment—don't make our country dirty," Bhuckory said. She related the time that she had a car accident and had to go to the police station to straighten out the resulting paperwork. At the end of it all, she went into the bathroom and found that the toilets smelled. "Is your home like this?" she asked the abashed police captain. She enrolled the station in a *Fleurir Maurice* contest and "now the barracks are like a garden."

As incentives, the movement gives its own awards, too. "An award is not only an honor, it is a challenge," Bhuckory said. What began with recognition for the planting of flowers and trees at sugar plantations has grown to roughly 100 award categories, including villages, beaches, police stations, schools, and government buildings. Juries visit every contest entrant to check its work.

The private movement has gained enough grassroots support to go head-to-head with government, if necessary. And a generation of Mauritians has been brought up to know the word "environment" and what it means to them personally.

A grassroots effort in the United States was spurred on by Global 500 laureate Andrew David Holleman, a resident of Chelmsford, Massachusetts. But he did not clean up an environmental mess—he prevented it from happening.

In 1987, the Holleman family received notice that the wetland woods near their home were going to be cut down and replaced by a 180-unit housing project. Holleman, who had played in the woods as a boy for many years, set forth to research the company's legal right to turn it into a housing complex.

Andrew David Holleman

Holleman's own housing district had been built on wetlands forty years previously, and he knew that the high water level led to basement flooding and unstable house foundations in the neighborhood. He wondered whether it was safe to construct another large housing project on top of the similar wetlands across from his home. And the fate of the wildlife that found refuge there was another major concern.

The Massachusetts native studied the regulations, called environmentalists for information, and prepared a tight case against the developers based on the polluting factor of building on wetlands. Holleman then started a petition to quash the project. He went to his neighbors, explained the housing project's danger to the town, and lobbied for their support. In a protracted fight, Holleman had one huge advantage over the millionaire lawyers who wanted to pave over the woods—he was only twelve years old.

The wealthy developers found themselves in a David-and-Goliath fight that soon got the townspeople, Massachusetts politicians, and finally environmentalists around the country to rally behind the boy. Holleman not only knew the technical issues. He also spoke of his beloved woods, the wonder of the flora and fauna found there, and what it meant to him and other children. "I practically grew up in those woods," he said. Newspapers and television stations soon picked up the story. Completely outgunned, the developers threw in the towel.

Holleman was fourteen years old when he was named to the Global 500 Roll of Honor in 1989. Following on the success of his first environmental battle, he travels the country, during time off from high school, to deliver a "you-can-do-it-too speech" to other young people. A well-organized and well-spoken young man, his inspirational message is based on a common-sense, five-point program: define your cause; get information and get it straight; stay local; seek publicity; and, above all, never give up.

13

Unshakable Faith

Religious hierarchies have been slow to adopt environmentalism as a moral issue. But long before these institutions began to join the environmental cause, many individuals brought their religious faith to bear on environmental issues in their own way.

Consider Phra Ajahn Pongsak Tejadhammo, a Buddhist monk and 1990 laureate. Phra Ajahn (a title of respect given to educators) has lived in the forests of Thailand for twenty-five of the thirty-eight years he has been a monk and has seen firsthand the impact of deforestation on people's lives. Monks are highly respected in Thai society, and people look to them for guidance in spiritual as well as practical matters such as medicine, education, and social concerns. Ajahn Pongsak has used his leadership role to educate villagers about sustainable resource management and to support conservation projects.

We traveled to Thailand to meet Ajahn Pongsak and visit his project area in the Mae Soi valley, an important watershed in the far north. The organization he founded—the Dhammanaat Foundation for Conservation and Rural Development—is based in the centuries-old city of Chiang Mai, but Ajahn Pongsak himself is often out at the project sight, either in the valley lowland being reforested or up on the ridgetop at the seedling nursery.

> *The forest is an organism of extraordinary benevolence. It gives freely of its produce. . . and asks for nothing in return. It does not withhold its shelter even from the axeman who would destroy it.*
> —**Mahayana Buddhist text**

It was on the ridgetop where we finally found him, after a

grinding drive by jeep up a steep dirt road that had turned to mud in a monsoon. Twice, all of us—author, foundation liaison, interpreter, and driver—had to get out and push the truck out of deep, slippery ruts caused by the erosion of the road. Finally, seated on tree stumps as we looked out over the misty valley below, Ajahn Pongsak explained his evolution into an environmental activist.

Ajahn Pongsak first visited the Mae Soi valley in 1968 to meditate in the natural shelter of the forest. When he came back eight years later, he was shocked at the deterioration. The government had given commercial concessions to harvest teak and other hardwoods; villagers had cut many trees for their supplies of fuelwood and building materials; and hill-tribe people—both indigenous people and refugees from Laos, Cambodia, Myanmar, and Vietnam—had slashed and burned trees on the steep slopes to grow subsistence crops of rice and maize and cash crops of opium. By 1977, according to the foundation, virtually all the trees in the valley had been cut down.

Along with the loss of trees, Ajahn Pongsak said, he noticed there were fewer monkeys and birds in the remaining forest. Then the local villagers came to him complaining they had no water and their crop yields were dwindling. Deforestation had caused massive erosion of the steep hillsides, siltation of streams, and loss of water absorption by the soil.

From his many years spent wandering through the forests of Thailand, Ajahn Pongsak was already well aware of the interdependence of natural ecosystems. That ethic was also part of the Buddhist philosophy he had been studying all his life. "Buddha always pointed out to his disciples that their livelihood depended on the forests," Ajahn Pongsak told us in his gentle voice. "But modern education now stresses how we can take from other people, other things. People just take and take and take and take" without thinking of what they must give back.

So he began to remind the villagers of the Buddhist principle of *silatham,* a concept they were already familiar with through Buddhist learnings but had not been practicing. The concept embraces the relationships among the individual, society, and nature. "It is all interdependent," Ajahn Pongsak said, gesturing to the denuded valley below. "When we protect the forest, we protect the world. When we destroy that balance, causing drastic changes in global weather and soil conditions, we cause severe hardship to the people

Ajahn Pongsak pauses and enjoys a moment of cheer during a visit by the authors. (Photograph by Elizabeth Lee)

. . . thus the forest is the creator of environmental *silatham*, ensuring a healthy harmony in people's lives both physically and mentally."

Ajahn Pongsak also helped the villagers implement practical solutions to their daily problems, such as procuring enough water. For example, he taught them how to build irrigation channels lined with cement to prevent seepage. Such solutions proved only temporary, however, as continuing deforestation further depleted natural water sources.

In Ajahn Pongsak's view, deforestation was not the root cause of the problem. The real cause, he said, was the "wrong attitudes" of everyone involved: the Royal Forestry Department, which owns all the forested land; businesses that reap profits from the felling of trees; and the hill-tribe people and valley villagers eking a living out of their deteriorating surroundings.

To change attitudes and campaign for forest conservation on a broad scale, Ajahn Pongsak set up the Dhammanaat Foundation in 1988. The foundation has three main objectives: conservation, rural development, and education. Its main venture, the Forest Village project at Mae Soi, covers about seventy square kilometers and encompasses eleven villages.

The project's goal is to wean villagers from dependence on cutting down the forests. On land loaned by the Forestry Department, villagers built a fourteen-kilometer fence to protect the watershed forests on the ridges, established a nursery to germinate thousands of locally collected native seeds, laid eleven kilometers of pipes for watering the seedlings, and planted 30,000 native pine, oak, chestnut, magnolia, teak, ironwood, and wild mango trees on the ridges and in the valley. They also maintain a twenty-four-hour forest patrol against hunting, felling, and burning in the dry season.

The foundation also gives educational seminars at the Meditation Center Ajahn Pongsak set up in the remaining forest at Mae Soi. The foundation plans to open a nature center, where visitors can learn the concepts of interdependence and harmony that Ajahn Pongsak has taught the local villagers.

The Mae Soi project is the first example in Thailand of cooperation between a religious organization and the government. The project's success has motivated villagers in neighboring valley catchments, comprising some 90,000 people, to follow suit.

While the foundation now has the support of the Royal Forestry Department, the government has not always taken such a kind view of Ajahn Pongsak's efforts. Once they sued him for "encroachment" in the very forests he is trying to protect. Now the Forestry Department, in addition to releasing degraded forest land to be developed as new Forest Villages, is also offering support in the way of machinery for construction of irrigation systems, technical advice, and seedlings for reforestation.

The foundation is still at odds, however, with the Department of the Interior over aid projects benefiting the hill tribes. To try to stop the flow of opium at its source, foreign aid organizations support projects that introduce substitute cash crops, such as cabbages and potatoes. But these require at least four times as much land as opium to be profitable, leading to further deforestation of the fragile ridgetops.

Although the hill tribes have profited greatly from the aid programs, the people in the valley have continued to suffer from the effects of deforestation. Ajahn Pongsak is patiently arguing for the hill tribes to relocate to the valley, and while he says they themselves have agreed to the move, the Department of the Interior—through which the aid money flows—will not allow it. During our visit in the summer of 1991, negotiations were still underway.

Being named to the Global 500 has meant a great deal to Ajahn Pongsak. "Conservationists in developing countries are powerless," he pointed out. "To carry on our work, it is important for us to meet other environmental activists with similar ideas." The award was also a message to him, he said, as well as to the government he often criticizes, that "I'm not fighting alone. It had an important impact on the government; it stunned them." Now they must be careful how they treat him, for they know others are watching and consider his work important.

Before Ajahn Pongsak received the award in 1990, the government did not allow any publicity of his activities. But with the landslide of attention brought on by the prize, there was nothing they could do to stop it. The publicity itself, Ajahn Pongsak explained, is also helpful to his work. It allows him "to be on stage," to let people know he is working for conservation.

The award also "has sparked the interest of other monks and [nongovernmental organizations] in Thailand to stand up, to fight for conservation," he said. The Association of Monks for Conservation and the Development of Life and the Environment, a support network for conservation-minded monks, chose him to serve as its president.

Another cleric who sees environmental protection as a religious obligation is Sister Aida Velasquez. One of this Philippine laureate's main goals has been to block the construction of a nuclear power plant planned for the rural province of Bataan. The plant was to be built near several volcanoes, on a major fault line prone to earthquakes. As of our writing, the effort has been successful, with construction halted and a major lawsuit in progress.

We met Sister Aida, a Benedictine nun, because of that success. She was invited to the U.N.-sponsored Global Assembly for Women and the Environment, held in Miami, Florida, in November 1991, to describe the ten-year grassroots campaign that defeated the plant.

Sister Aida's involvement with the antinuclear cause began back in 1976, after she moved to Bataan. She had asked to be assigned there because she was interested in how local farmers were coping with their new factory jobs in the recently industrialized region.

Before she became a nun in 1966, Sister Aida had received an undergraduate degree in chemical engineering from Mapua Institute of Technology in Manila, a masters in chemistry from the University of Detroit in Michigan, and worked for eighteen months as a chemist at the International Rice Research Institute. Because of her background, a local parish priest asked her to come to a meeting of villagers and tell them about nuclear energy.

It was the villagers' first inkling of the hazards of nuclear energy, and they became alarmed. Weighing the benefits of "clean" energy against the risks of thermal pollution to their fishing grounds, radiation from the plant, and radioactive waste, they decided to oppose the plant.

They planned a village-to-village campaign to inform their neighbors of the nuclear risks. On the first day, shortly before an informational meeting was to be held, the village head told the group they would need a permit to meet. Since it had to be acquired in a nearby city and the last bus of the day had already left, it was impossible to get the permit in time. At this point the group realized that the local officials did not support the campaign.

The people persevered, though, and began photocopying materials and passing them around secretly to friends and relatives. Sister Aida realized, however, that they needed more information and wider support. She began networking with professional, religious, social, and human rights groups in Manila. That led in 1977 to the formation of the Philippine Movement for Environment Protection (PMEP), which issued a position paper against the power plant and distributed it to other groups around the country. The PMEP in turn helped form the Nuclear Free Philippines Coalition, which orchestrated much of the campaign.

What allowed the effort to go public without facing prosecution was a typhoon that hit the Philippine island of Mindanao in 1979. Local newspaper articles began raising the question of whether the Bataan plant, being constructed by the U.S. company Westinghouse, would be able to withstand this kind of storm. President Marcos then promised to get safety assurances from Westinghouse and to cancel the contract if those assurances were not forthcoming.

This dialogue gave people the opportunity to write to Marcos asking him to cancel the contract immediately. At this stage, the Sierra Club and the Natural Resources Defense Council, both private U.S. environmental organizations, became involved, pressing the U.S. Congress to regulate the export of the nuclear reactor and related technology.

Then in 1981 came the highly publicized accident at the Three Mile Island nuclear plant in the United States. Some well-known Filipinos came out publicly against building such a plant in their own country. Sister Aida joined with these new voices, and gave information to a newly appointed government commission formed to study the plant. It determined that while the site was safe, the plant's structure itself was not, and construction was delayed.

The power plant became a national issue. Sister Aida says the cause drew widespread support among many diverse constituencies because it involved questions of justice, peace, human rights, and health as well as the environment.

The plant became a campaign issue in 1986, with Corazon Aquino promising to scrap the project if she were elected. She won and kept her word. Following the Chernobyl nuclear accident in April of that year, work on the plant—estimated to cost $2.2 billion, with $35,000 being paid each day in interest on a loan taken out for the project—was finally stopped.

When we talked with Sister Aida, the Philippine government was in the process of suing Westinghouse, citing evidence that the company bribed former President Marcos to get the contract. Sister Aida, who was still following the issue, said Westinghouse made an offer, for an undisclosed amount, to settle out of court, but at press time it was still under study.

Throughout the evolving situation, Sister Aida told us, her role was "to keep the flow of information going among the different groups." It was a task she took on despite some physical risk. Although the group tried to keep its activities secret, Sister Aida feared that her role might be known to some government officials. Friends warned her not to travel alone, telling her that policemen sometimes asked women traveling on buses if they were Aida Velasquez. "I was a bad word" to people working on the power plant, she said. "I was not afraid, but I didn't take unnecessary risks."

"I did not plan on this thing," she added. "It was a spontaneous reaction of Filipinos against such an expensive, hazardous reactor which our people could ill afford," especially considering the basic human needs that were not being addressed.

Sister Aida has been involved in other environmental efforts as well. For example, she joined in the ongoing campaign against the pollution of Calancan Bay, where a mining company has been dumping tailings. "The bay used to be a rich fishing ground," she said, "with numerous coral reefs, but both the coral and the fish have disappeared because of the pollution, impoverishing the fishermen in the area, most of whom could not send their children to school, especially to college. Young people left to find jobs elsewhere as they could hardly catch enough fish for family consumption, and the fish caught were said to be contaminated." Unfortunately, despite growing local opposition to the practice, the dumping continued.

In 1985 Sister Aida founded a nongovernmental organization called *Lingkod Tao-Kalikasan*, or "In the Service of the Human-Earth Community." Through seminars, pamphlets, and a newsletter, the group promotes ecological awareness in the Philippines, a country made up of 7,100 mostly small and ecologically vulnerable islands. "We are encouraging individuals to do their share in protecting their environment, to see it as part of the global struggle to keep our planet viable," Sister Aida explained. "It is part of my Christian mission."

The Global 500 award "affirmed the legitimacy of this work," which she termed "urgent and essential." She said, "My mission in life is to do what God wants me to do, which at the moment is to help protect the environment, to help protect the Earth. If we do not protect the environment, poverty will worsen. If God is concerned with the poor, then I am sure He does not want the poor to be any poorer.

"Our islands are dying because we have removed the forests, hence the agricultural productivity of our farmlands has gone down. Our mangroves and corals have been destroyed, so there are not many fish to catch in the sea. Meanwhile, our population is growing . . . Once the islands turn to deserts, what will happen to all of us, and to the rest of Filipinos yet to be born?"

14

Salt of the Earth

The protection of the vast African, Asian, and Latin American backlands has been largely left to the world's poor—those most vulnerable to environmental degradation, least equipped to change their circumstances, and most likely to spoil tomorrow's habitat to survive today's exigencies.

Global 500 farmers who plant trees, terrace their small plots, and prudently manage limited water supplies are the unheralded foot-soldiers of the worldwide struggle for sustainable development. Laureate Mark Dokotela Ncube is such a farmer.

"Come see," shouted Ncube as we approached his small farmhouse. The seventy-year-old Zimbabwean had much to show. He had taken unpromising communal scrubland and turned it into a verdant oasis. "Ncube has shown how wise conservation contributes to successful farm production," explained a young extension worker from the Department of Natural Resources.

"I manufactured this farm with my hands," Ncube said. But he also used his head. In 1950 he left teaching, which paid poorly, to take up farming. The teacher's education gave him the ability to absorb new ideas and gain access to a larger world of information than his immediate surroundings provided.

From the outset, Ncube concentrated on improving the quality of his small plot rather than, like his neighbors, attempting to use more and more land. With dogged determination and backbreaking labor, he began to terrace his eroded land, creating level plots by importing the soil stored in nearby abandoned anthills. Each plot was leveled, squared off, and protected against erosion by a combi-

Farmers in Burkina Faso, West Africa, watch a demonstration showing the effectiveness of 'stone lines' to control erosion. The farmers use stakes and water-filled plastic tubes to indicate the level contours, and build stone lines along them. (Photograph © by Mark Edwards/Still Pictures)

nation of plantings and wood and cement barriers. In some places, he would pile up as much as a meter of new topsoil on the washboard surface of the orginal land to level it off. Year after year he laborously terraced his land.

A reliable source of water, an essential element in short supply in the semi-arid area, was slowly developed. First, the determined Zimbabwean tapped an underground spring. Then he contrived an irrigation system. Laboriously, he built storage pools, dug irrigation ditches, constructed viaducts, and channeled water to seep prudently from one terrace to another.

Ncube lost few opportunities to improve his land. Banana trees were planted and watered by bucket. Once they took root, they were able to retain what water came their way naturally. Fish were stocked in one of the pools to provide a new food source. Trees were planted and nurtured until they could grow tall and straight, thereby providing fruit, shade, and protection against erosion.

The former school-teacher-turned-farmer experimented with seedlings and carefully selected good cattle for breeding to upgrade his small herd. Wood for fencing, poles, tomato stakes, and the like were dried in the sun, saved, and reused, instead of the usual practice of throwing away wood and cutting more later when the seasonal need arose.

Annually the land was meticulously prepared by an ox-drawn plow and seeds were carefully planted by hand. As more and more land was slowly made fruitful, Ncube's income rose, allowing him to hire some labor, improve his seed, and acquire amenities for his simple house.

Ncube won the Zimbabwe Natural Resources Certificate of Merit in 1983, which brought interest to his work. But he said it was not until after he was placed on the Global 500 Roll of Honor in 1990 that government ministers, journalists, and other curious onlookers began visiting his farm in full force. He now enjoys some celebrity for his difficult labor.

"Determination made this farm bloom," he contended. "Others could do the same." To demonstrate his point, he has left a couple of strips of land in their original state to make a before-and-after contrast with the rest of the farm.

Ncube's meticulous farming is exceptional, and so is his dedication to education. He has put his six children through school. But they, like untold millions in the world, have left the countryside to live in cities. And Ncube works communal lands, which means that his children cannot hope to inherit his farm without returning home, something he knows none of them is inclined to do.

The aging Zimbabwean, then, is working almost exclusively for personal pride and progress. He delights in showing the certificates bestowing upon him the titles of "Master Farmer" and "Master of Tillage." Ncube, whose eyesight is beginning to fail, still works his farm with all the energy he can muster. In a guest book, one visiter penned: "Mark Dokotela Ncube left teaching to become a farmer; now he teaches the world the value of conservation."

Two other Zimbabwean farmers and Global 500 laureates, Pamuchigere Nembire and Nyamuniwa Nyamundo, suggest that there is a potential for tapping grassroots environmental farming that goes beyond a few isolated examples like Ncube.

Nembire is a traditional chief who converted some of his tribal lands into an ecologically sound farming area. The lands were marginal at best, degraded by the civil strife engendered by the long fight to create an independent, biracial government. Nembire espoused basic conservation—sustainable agriculture, soil protection, prudent use of water, and tree planting—to rejuvenate his farm and the surrounding area.

His labor has brought incremental improvement to the land. He has prepared four hectares for planting of nonindigenous trees and protection of the local forest; planted two-and-one-half hectares with tobacco for cash income; added two new fish ponds to the existing one; and encouraged the community to come up with sustainable grazing schemes.

Nyamundo has neither Ncube's education nor Nembire's automatic prestige, but he did demonstrably improve his six-hectare farm by many of the same painstaking methods his countrymen use—tree planting, soil improvement, fish ponds, and water management.

When he started, doubting neighbors contended that he "was wasting his time in the hot sun." But the tree planting and sustainable farming methods eventually paid off in ways that could not be ignored. The local children enjoyed sharing the fruit from his trees, and word of Nyamundo's effective methods soon spread. When his neighbors heard that he received the 1991 Global 500 award, there was great celebration, and his reputation as a miracle worker was secure.

In Stockholm, Nyamundo received his award certificate from the King of Sweden in a grand hall. Nyamundo was clearly pleased. But because his English was so scant, he could scarcely explain to his hosts what it meant for a poor, undereducated farmer from a remote African village to receive international recognition for his hard work and care for his surroundings.

The Global 500 Roll of Honor includes various grassroots champions of environmentally sound and productive farming from around the world:

- Landless Indian farmer Harekala Moideen led a poor farmers' movement to clear a swamp and create a fruit plantation in its stead. Clearing wetlands, we should note, is not necessarily a favor to the ecosystem in the long term, even though it was unquestionably an immediate improvement for Moideen and his neighbors.
- Agronomist Basil Allen Rossi showed Filipino peasants how to increase their sugar, rice, and pepper crops by as much as 300 percent by introducing organic farming.
- Jose Manuel Salazar, a Colombian *campesino*, has turned his small farm into a demonstration project by planting trees on his land and teaching his neighbors how to follow suit.
- Ven Kirantidiye Pannnasekera Thero, a Sri Lankan Buddhist monk, rallied 1,000 villagers to fight off development projects that threatened their land. He also mounted a local afforestation program and converted a small village into a model of sustainable development.
- Bernard Ledea Ouedraogo, of Burkina Faso, is cited as the "driving force" behind an association of 700 Sahelian village groups that form an association that "promotes environmentally sound small-scale projects, including water conservation, afforestation and grain storage." Aminata Wade, from Senegal, is similarly cited.
- Chinese laureate Zhen-Lin Zhang's work received a 1987 award as "a model for renewable energy development." He-hang Village was also cited. The collective actions of Chinese villages, which hold three-quarters of the nation's massive population of more than 1.2 billion,

> will go a long way toward deciding what kind of environment the world will have.

It is critical that people in so-called "developed" countries tone down their lifestyles, which are so dependent on high and thoughtless consumption of the world's natural resources, but it is also important that Third World citizens realize the standard model of development is destructive. If the rural poor of the world were to pursue that model of progress, it would blow a global fuse.

We cannot note here all the thumbnail sketches of the grassroots environmentalists who have been named to the Global 500. But to recognize those who make a big difference in a small way, we invite you to look up the award citations in the back of the book.

Afterword

The Global 500 laureates are an exotic mix of grassroots environmentalists, august scientists, national movements, international institutions, private companies, and politicos. One of the most striking aspects of the Global 500 process is how well the laureates, particularly those on the grassroots level, interact when meeting each other at the annual awards ceremonies.

Most grassroots laureates work in great isolation from the global environmental movement. Often they are the object of ridicule, hostility, or at best, indifference. When they meet at the ceremonies, they are overwhelmed by the realization that they have like-minded counterparts around the world who face similar problems and share the same visions.

During the awards ceremonies many of the winners try to form an ongoing relationship. But when they go back home, more often than not they return to their relative isolation. UNEP has made an effort to keep the laureates in contact through a newsletter produced by Phillip Noyce, an active Australian laureate.

Called *Global 500 Newsletter*, the quarterly, which has an annual subscription rate of $40, is a clearinghouse for laureate activities and opinions. Noyce, with widespread support among the laureates, is also pushing the idea of a Global 500 Action Forum to give the laureates a cohesive voice in the international environmental debate.

Phillip Noyce
Editor, *Global 500 Newsletter*
PO Box 16
North Melbourne 3051
Australia
Fax: (61-3) 328-4445

As time goes on, the Roll of Honor grows. The 1992 ceremony brings the number of laureates to 500, but despite its name, the Global 500 will continue to add new honorees for the foreseeable future. Can the growing number of laureates—who speak different languages, pursue distinct and often contradictory goals, and come from such diverse cultures—form a cohesive international environmental movement? We certainly hope so.

UNEP officials wish to further institutionalize the award and make it more widely known throughout the world. To assist the process, we offer in the following pages the names and addresses of all Global 500 laureates awarded so far and a sample nomination form.

The Global 500 Roll of Honor

Beyene Abadi
c/o 'Hebret'
PO Box 247
Asmara
ETHIOPIA

Nijaz Abadzic
Glise Jankovica 2/II
Ilidza-Sarajevo 71210
YUGOSLAVIA

Martin Abraham
International Organization
of Consumers Union
26N Green Lane
Penang 11 600
MALAYSIA

Ahmed Adel-Gawaad
PO Box 613
El-Maadi
Cairo
EGYPT

Adebayo Adeola
PO Box 4185
Ibadan
NIGERIA

Anil Agarwal
Centre for Science
and Environment
F7 Kalaish Colony
New Delhi 110048
INDIA

Yusuf J. Ahmad
PO Box 47074
Nairobi
KENYA

Dr. Ahmed Abdel Rahman Al-Agib
Faculty of Applied Science
PO Box 326671
BAHRAIN

Badria Abdullah Al-Awadi
ROPME
PO Box 26388
Safat
KUWAIT

Roland Albignac
UNESCO
c/o PNUD, UNESCO
BP 1346
Antananarivo
MADAGASCAR

Alcoa of Australia Limited
GPO Box 4866
Melbourne 3000
AUSTRALIA

Abdulbar Al-Gain
Meteorology and
Environmental Protection
Administration
PO Box 1358
Jeddah
SAUDI ARABIA

Jassim Mohammed Al-Hassan
Faculty of Science
Kuwait University
Safat
KUWAIT

Maria Helena Allegretti
IEA
Rua Monte Castelo, 380
Curitiba - Parana 82500
BRAZIL

Irma Acosta Allen
PO Box 135
Mbabane
SWAZILAND

Gaetano Allotta
Lega Navale Italiana
Via Diodoro Siculo
Agrigento
ITALY

Azaria Alon
SPNI
4 Hashfela Street
Tel-Aviv 66183
ISRAEL

Miguel Alvarez del Toro
Apdo, Postal No. 6
Tuxtla Gutierrez
Chiapas
MEXICO

Pablo Amaringo
Escuela de Pintura Amazonica
Usko-Ayar
Giron Sanchez Cerro 465-467
Pucallpa
PERU

Amasachina Self-Help Association
PO Box 798
Tamale, Northern Region
GHANA

Amigos Da Natureza
CP 62
St. Vincente
CAPE VERDE

Murlidar 'Baba' Devidas Amte
Anandway, via Warora
Maharastra 442 914
INDIA

Roula Angelakis-Malakis
Gynaika
25 Gennadiou Street
Athens 16341
GREECE

Arab Office for Youth and Environment
PO Box 49, Manail el Roda
Cairo
EGYPT

Joaquin Araujo
Av. America 8
Madrid 28028
SPAIN

Arthur Archer
172 Regency Park
Christ Church
BARBADOS

George Archibald
International Crane Foundation
E- 11376 Shady Lane Road
Baraboo, WI 53913-9778
USA

Nikki Ashley
Wildlife Conservation Society of Zambia
PO Box 30255
Lusaka 10101
ZAMBIA

David Attenborough
BBC/TV
London
UNITED KINGDOM

Adel Awad
Faculty of Civil Engineering
Tishreen University
Lattakia
SYRIA

Theodore Epey Ayuk Oben
Club des Amis de la Nature
University de Yaounde,
BP 836
Yaounde
CAMEROON

Baha'i Vocational Institute for Women
180 Bhamori
New Dewas Road
Indore MP 452008
INDIA

Bamburi Portland Cement Co Ltd
Baobab Farm Ltd
PO Box 90202
Mombasa
KENYA

Brigitte Bardot
Fondation Brigitte Bardot
4 Rue Franklin
Z5116 Paris
FRANCE

Mohamed Siad Barre
Presidency Office
Mogadishu
SOMALIA

Charley Barretto
Science of Mind
and Man Center
Gold Building
15 Annapolis Street
Greenhills
Metro Manila
PHILIPPINES

Rita Barron
Charles River Watershed Association
76 Waldon Street
Newtonville, MA 02160
USA

Parbati Baruah
c/o UNEP Regional Office
UN Building
Rajdamnern Avenue
Bangkok 10200
THAILAND

Biplab B. Basu
School of Fundamental
Research
49B - Tolly Gunge Road
Calcutta 700 026
INDIA

Kamal H. Batanouny
Faculty of Science
Cairo University
EGYPT

Michel Batisse
9, Avenue Leonce-Bucquet
Garches 92380
FRANCE

BAUM
Tinsdateer Kirchenweg 211
Hamburg 56 2000
GERMANY

Carlos Minc Baumfield
PADE
rua P Cesar de Andrade,
222-Ap 802 Laranderes
Rio de Janeiro 22221
BRAZIL

Purevjavyn Bayarsaikhan
Mongolian Radio Broadcasting
IY District 12/324
Ulaanbaatar
MONGOLIA

Jean M. Belanger
Canadian Chemical
Producers Association
Suite 805, 350 Sparks Street
Ottawa
CANADA

David Bellamy
Durham University
Co. Durham DL13 3NN
UNITED KINGDOM

Bellerive Foundation
PO Box 42994
Nairobi
KENYA

Enrique Beltram
Cerrania 219 Insurgentes Cuicuilco
Mexico DF 04530
MEXICO

George Benneh
Department of Geography and
Resource Development
PO Box 59
Legon
Accra
GHANA

H.R.H. Prince Bernhard
WWF-Netherlands
PO Box 7
Zeist 3700 AA
THE NETHERLANDS

Chandi Prasad Bhatt
Dasholi Gram Swarajya
Mandal
Gopeshwar
District Chamoli, UP 246401
INDIA

Chandranee Bhuckory
Fleurir Maurice
Mauritius Government Tourist Office
Emmanuel Anquetil Building
Port Louis
MAURITIUS

Gertrude Duby Blom
Na-Bolom, Av. Vicenze Guerro 33
San Cristonal De Las Casas
Chiapas 29220
MEXICO

Michael Bloomfield
Harmony Foundation of Canada
225-501 Metcalfe Street
Ottawa, Ontario K2P 1P9
CANADA

Francis Boateng
Ghana National Fire Service
PO Box 4129
Accra
GHANA

Bombay Natural History Society (BNHS)
Hornbill House
(Museum Compound)
Shaheed Bhagat Singh Road
Bombay 400023
INDIA

Alexander Bonilla
Fundacion Ecodesarrollo
Apartado 6732/100
San Jose
COSTA RICA

Dr. Francois Bourliere
Faculty of Medicine
University of Paris
15 Avenue de Tourville
Paris 75007
FRANCE

Jim Brandenburg
Brandenburg Photography
126 N 3rd Street #308
Minneapolis, MN 55401
USA

Paul Adrian Brodeur
The New Yorker
23 West 43rd Street
New York, NY 10036
USA

Dr. Bob Brown
Green Independents
Parliament House
Hobart 7000
AUSTRALIA

Lester Brown
WorldWatch Institute
1776 Massachusetts Avenue NW,
Suite 701
Washington, DC 20036
USA

Gro Harlem Brundtland
Prime Minister
Parliament House
Oslo
NORWAY

Kenneth A. Brynaert
200-f Woodridge Crescent
Ottawa K2B 7S9
CANADA

Reid A. Bryson
11 Rosewood Circle
Madison, WI 53711
USA

Mohammad Ilyas Burney
213/3 Ordnance Road
Rawalpindi Cant.
PAKISTAN

Robert J. Burton
Department of Mining
Tasmanian Wilderness Society
130 Davey Street
Hobart 7000
AUSTRALIA

Paul John Butler
Forest and Land Department
Castries 809 45 23231
ST. LUCIA

Charles Caccia
House of Commons
Room 3535, Centre Block
Ottawa KLA OA6
CANADA

Keith Caldwell
4898 D Heritage Woods Road
Bloomington, IN 47401
USA

Idelisa de Calventi Bonnelly
Guarocuya No. 90, El Millon Santo
Domingo
DOMINICAN REPUBLIC

Jorge Cappato
Centro de Proteccion a la Naturaleza
Casilla de Correo 550
(300) Santa Fe
ARGENTINA

Care-International
600 First Avenue
New York, NY 10016
USA

Caribbean Conservation Association
Savannah Lodge
The Garrison
St. Michael
BARBADOS

Jimmy Carter
Richard B. Russell Building
75 Spring Street SW
Atlanta, GA 30303
USA

Cetacean Society International
190 Stillwold Drive
Wethersfield, CT 06109
USA

Chul-whan Cha
Korea University 4,
Institute for Environmental Health
2-ga Myungyun-dong,
Congro-Gu
Seoul
REPUBLIC OF KOREA

Gabrial L. Charles
c/o Forestry Department
Ministry of Agriculture, Castries
St. Lucia, Windward Islands
LESSER ANTILLES

Chengdu Zoo
Huanxin Jue Province, Chengdu City
Sichuan Province
PEOPLE'S REPUBLIC OF CHINA

Maria V. Cherkasova
Socio-Ecological Union
Malaya Bronnaya 12, Apt 12
Moscow 103104
RUSSIAN FEDERATION

Children's Alliance for the Protection of the Environment
8117 Greenwich Meridian
Austin, TX 78759
USA

Chatichai Choonhaven
Government House
Bangkok 10300
THAILAND

Brian Clark
University of Aberdeen
Aberdeen
SCOTLAND

Anthony Brian Cleaver
IBM UK Ltd
PO Box 41, North Harbour
Portsmouth, Hants PO6 3AU
UNITED KINGDOM

CODDEFFAGOLF
Casa No. 1528
Ave. Los Inditos
Bo. Los Profesores
Comayaguela
HONDURAS

College of African Wildlife Management
MWEKA, PO Box 3031
Moshi
TANZANIA

Commission for the Future
98 Drummond Street
Carlton 3053
AUSTRALIA

Commonwealth Scientific & Industrial Research Organization
Private Bag #1
Mordialloc 3195
AUSTRALIA

Conservation Council of New Brunswick
180 St. John Street
Fredericton, New Brunswick
CANADA

Conservation International
1015 18th Street NW,
Suite 1000
Washington, DC 20036
USA

Hernan M. Contreras
CATIE
Turrialba
COSTA RICA

Whina Cooper
Panguru
The Hokianga
Northland
NEW ZEALAND

Keith Frederick Corbett
Pinetree Lodge, 30
Endfield Road, Moordown
Bournemouth, Dorset
UNITED KINGDOM

Rose Cotta
Soroptimist Club
c. Dr. Carulla 31-33, atico
08017 Barcelona
SPAIN

Michel Courtot
BP 1216
Noumea
NEW CALEDONIA

Jacques-Yves Cousteau
Cousteau Society Center
930 West 21st St.
Norfolk, VA 23517
USA

Rogelio Cova Juarez
Centro de Educacion
Ambiental y Accion Ecolog
Apartado Postal #30,
Calpulalpan
Tlaxcala 90200
MEXICO

Luc Cuyvers
The Mare Nostrum
Foundation
93 Main Street, Suite 400
Annapolis, MD 21401
USA

Czech National Union of Nature
Staromestske nam. 12
Prague
CZECHOSLOVAKIA

Bedrettin Dalan
Istanbul Belediyes
Aksaray
Istanbul
TURKEY

Sheila Gwennifer Davis
Native Forests Action
Council
Crewenna, Wakapuaka
RDI Nelson
NEW ZEALAND

Tuenjai Deetes
PO Box 11, Mae Chan
Chiang Rai 57110
THAILAND

Andreas Demetrion Demetropoulos
Ministry of Agriculture
and Natural Resources
PO Box 4281
Nicosia
CYPRUS

Maitraye Devi
13/1 Palm Avenue
Calcutta 19
INDIA

DHDK (Soc. Protection Wildlife in Turkey)
PO Box 18, Bebek
Istanbul
TURKEY

Diario El Comercio
Jiron Miro Quesada 304
Lima
PERU

Francesco di Castri
UNESCO
7 Place de Fontenoy
75700 Paris
FRANCE

Dominica Conservation Association
c/o Forestry Division
Roseau
DOMINICA

Paljor Dorje
High Court
Thimphu
BHUTAN

Nikolai Nikolaevich Drozdov
Faculty of Geography
Moscow State University
Moscow 119899
RUSSIAN FEDERATION

Rene Dumont
1 Rue Clos d'Orleans
Fontenay s/Bois 94120
FRANCE

Milo Dunphy
113 Mimi Street
Oatley 2253
AUSTRALIA

Gerald Durrell
Jersey Wildlife Preservation Trust
Jersey, Channel Islands
UNITED KINGDOM

The Dutch Cyclists' Union
(Fietserbond ENFB)
PO Box 2150
3440 DD Woerden
THE NETHERLANDS

Earthwatch Radio
University of Wisconsin-Madison
550 North Park Street
15 Science Hall
Madison, WI 53706
USA

Salwa Osman Ebeid
c/o UNSO/SUD/85X01 UNDP
PO Box 913
Khartoum
SUDAN

Ecology Law Quarterly
School of Law
University of California
Berkeley, CA 94720
USA

Mark Edwards
Still Pictures
199A Shooters Hill Road
London SE3 84L
UNITED KINGDOM

Anne & Paul Ehrlich
Department of Biological Sciences
Stanford University
Stanford, CA 94305
USA

Fatma El-Gohary
20 Soliman Abazza Street
Dokki
Gaza
EGYPT

Yasin El Hag Abdin
PO Box 2718
Khartoum
SUDAN

Anton Eliassen
Norwegian Meteorological Institute
PO Box 43, Blindern
Oslo 3 N-0313
NORWAY

John Elkington
SustainAbility Limited
The People's Hall,
91-97 Freston Road
London W11 4BD
UNITED KINGDOM

Olfat Dessouky Elsebaie
165 El Horria Avenue
Alexandria
EGYPT

Environment Telephone of Vereniging Milieudef
Damsak 26
Amsterdam 1012 LJ
THE NETHERLANDS

Environmental Committee of Limassol
Ria Fereou Street 53
Limassol
CYPRUS

Environmental Education Group of Chaozhou Ci
No. 7, Xiyuan Road
Chaozhou, Guangdong
PEOPLE'S REPUBLIC OF CHINA

Environmental Health
2-ga Myungyun-dong,
Congro-Gu
Seoul
REPUBLIC OF KOREA

Environmental Management Journal
Springer-Verlag New York Inc.
175 Fifth Avenue
New York, NY 10010
USA

Environmental Protection Society
c/o ROPME, PO Box 26388
Safat 13124
KUWAIT

City Council of Erlangen
Erlangen, Bavaria
GERMANY

Bu Eroh
Pasir Kadu
West Java
INDONESIA

Hussain Muhammad Ershad
President's Secretariat
Dhaka
BANGLADESH

Jairo Escobar
Comision Permanente del Pacifico Sur
Casilla 16638 Agencia 6400-9
Santiago
CHILE

Malin Falkenmark
Natural Science Research Council
PO Box 6711
S-11385 Stockholm
SWEDEN

Joseph C. Farman
British Antarctic Survey
Natural Environment Research
Council
Cambridge
UNITED KINGDOM

Anwar Fazel
PO Box 1045
Penang 10830
MALAYSIA

Philip Martin Fearnside
INPA
CP 487, Manaus-Amazonas
Amazon
BRAZIL

Fabio Jose Feldmann
Av. Brigadeiro Luis Antonio 4.442
Sao Paulo
BRAZIL

Gert Roland Fischer
PAN
PO Box 947, Joinville
Santa Catarina 89200
BRAZIL

Florence Fisher
Environmental Resources Limited
RD 1 Box 222
Chatham, NY 12037
USA

Perin Savakshaw Fitter
The Field of Environment
Conservation
Kenya Youth Association Council
PO Box 1690
Kisumu
KENYA

Vladimir Flint
Research Institute of Nature
Conservation
Znamenskoye-SadkiMoscow 113628
RUSSIAN FEDERATION

Jose Maussan Flota
'60 minutos', Televisa, S.A. de C.V.
Av. Chapultpec x 18, 2 Piso, Col.
Doctores
Mexico D.F. 006724
MEXICO

Ivan Fonseca
Rua Pocas de Caldas
165 Nanugue
Minas Gerais
BRAZIL

Joaquin Fonseca
Comision Permanente del Pacifico Sur
Calle 76, No. 9-88
Bogota
COLOMBIA

Walter Fontana
Fundacion de Accion Ecologica
Connect Casilla de Correo 519,
Codigo Postal
Cordoba
ARGENTINA

Friends of Trees of Living Beings
At/Po-Kesarpur, Via Mandhatapur,
District Puri
Orissa 752079
INDIA

FUDENA
c/o Transversal, Edifico Centro
Empresarial
Aptdo Postal 70376
Caracas 1071A
VENEZUELA

Kathryn S. Fuller
World Wildlife Fund - US
3718 Morrison Street, NW
Washington, DC 20015
USA

Grigory Galazii
Commission for UNEP GKNT
11 Gorky Street
K-9 Moscow 103905
RUSSIAN FEDERATION

German Garcia-Duran
Ambassador of Colombia
PO Box 48494
Nairobi
KENYA

Garoua College of Wildlife
Ecole de Faune, BP 271
Garoua
CAMEROON

Franjo Gasparovic
Kraljevac 14
Zagreb 4100
CROATIA

His Excellency President Maumoon Abdul Gayoom
The Republic of the Maldives Male
THE MALDIVES

Theodore Geisel
c/o Jed Mattes
40 West 57th Street, 6th Floor
New York, NY 10019
USA

Murray Gell-Mann
California Institute of Technology
Pasadena, CA 91125
USA

Dhrubajyoti Ghosh
Institute for Wetlands Management
370/1P NSC Bose Road
Calcutta 700047
INDIA

Bjorn Olov Gillberg
Mijocedrum, 14
S-756 48 Uppsala
SWEDEN

Herbert Girardet
93 Cambridge Gardens
London W.10
UNITED KINGDOM

Dr. Michael Glantz
National Center for Atmospheric Research
PO Box 3000
Boulder, CO 80307
USA

Joseph Glascott
c/o Sydney Morning Herald
235 Jones Street
Broadway 2008
AUSTRALIA

Golden Hope Plantations Berhad
Tingkat 9–16
Menara PNB
201-A, Jalan Tun Razak
50400 Kuala Lumpur
MALAYSIA

Edgardo Gomez
Marine Science Institute
UP PO Box 1, Diliman
Quezon City 1101
PHILIPPINES

Legeia Gonzalez
EIPMA
Calle 2oe No. 2-46 A. A. 2741
Cali
COLOMBIA

Julian Gonsalves
IIRR
Silang
Cavite 4118
PHILIPPINES

Niki Goulandris
Goulandris Natural History Museum
13 Levidou St.
Kifissia 145 62
GREECE

Greenbelt Movement
PO Box 67545
Nairobi
KENYA

Green Great Wall Group
c/o National Environment Protection Agency
Beijing
PEOPLE'S REPUBLIC OF CHINA

Greenpeace International
Temple House
25-26 High Street
Lewes
UNITED KINGDOM

Juan Grau
Instituto de Ecologia de Chile
Agustinas 641 - DPTO 11
Santiago de Chile
CHILE

Miguel Grinberg
Promundo
Casilla 60-Suc 14
Buenos Aires 1414
ARGENTINA

Grupo de Los Cien
Sierra Jiutepec 155-B
Lomas Barrilacao
Mexico D. F. 11010
MEXICO

Edwidge Guillon
"Le Boulay"
Conflans/Anille
72120 St. Calais
FRANCE

Julia Hailes
SustainAbility Limited
The People's Hall
91-97 Freston Road
London W11 4BD
UNITED KINGDOM

Youssef Halim
Department of Oceanography
University of Alexandria Alexandria
EGYPT

John Fagan Handley
The Groundwork Trust
2 Arlington Way
Wilmslow, Cheshire SK9 3BP
UNITED KINGDOM

Paul Harrison
IIED
3 Endsleigh Street
London WClH 0DD
UNITED KINGDOM

Michio Hashimoto
2-201 Aobadai
Midori-Ku Yokohama
JAPAN

Parvez Hassan
Hassan and Hassan
11B Danepur Road
Lahore
PAKISTAN

Ivan L. Head
International Development Research Centre
PO Box 8500
Ottawa, Ontario KlG 3H9
CANADA

Heheng Village
Jiangsu Province
Tai Country
PEOPLE'S REPUBLIC OF CHINA

Richard A. Hellman
2013 Q Street, NW
Washington, DC 20009
USA

Donald James Henry
World Wildlife Fund - Australia
Level 17, St. Martins Tower, Market Street
Sydney 2000
AUSTRALIA

Jorge Ignacio Hernandez Camacho
Calle 39 18A-14
Bogota
COLOMBIA

Hetian County Government
Xinjiang Uighur Autonomous Region
PEOPLE'S REPUBLIC OF CHINA

Catherine Hicks
c/o Cetacean Society International
190 Stillwold Drive
Wethersfield, CT 06109
USA

High Country News
Paonia, CO
USA

Gome Gnohite Hilaire
President, Croix Verte
02 Bp 699 Abidjan 02
COTE d'IVOIRE

Sir Edmund Hillary
278A Remuera Road
Remuera
NEW ZEALAND

Kazuo Hishida
1-6-6 Komoba
Meguroku
Tokyo
JAPAN

Thilo Walter Hoffmann
Wildlife and Nature Protection Soc.
Sri Lanka
29, Baur's Flats
Colombo 1
SRI LANKA

Dr. Martin Holdgate
Director-General, IUCN
Avenue du Mont-Blanc
Gland CH-1196
SWITZERLAND

Andrew Holleman
26 Judith Road
Chelmsford, MA 01824
USA

David J. Holm
2012 Mapleton Street
Boulder, CO 80302
USA

Dr. Sidney Holt
GIOF
Podere il Falco
Citta della Pieve (PG) 06062
ITALY

Soichiro Honda
Honda Motors Co Ltd
27-8 Jingumai, 6-Chome, Shibuyaoku
Tokyo
JAPAN

Hoogovens Aluminium
(Huettenwerk GmbH)
Postfack 100, Schleusen
Voerde D-4223
GERMANY

Riel Huarani
Rock Petjomaltest
Scuola Europea Ingenieria
Villa Reale Borbonica Q,
Castellamare di Stablia
Naples
ITALY

Victoria Husband
PO Box 10, RR#5
Durrance Road
Victoria BC V8X 4M6
CANADA

Kazi Zakar Hussain
University of Dhaka
38/D, Issakhan Road
Dhaka 1000
BANGLADESH

Satu Huttunen
University of Oulu
Faculty of Natural Science
Oulu SF 90100
FINLAND

Institute of Desert Research
Academia Sinica
Lanzhou
PEOPLE'S REPUBLIC OF CHINA

Institute of Tropical Forestry
USDA Forest Service
Call Box 2500
Rio Piedras 00928 2500
PUERTO RICO

Instituto Forestal Latino Americano
Apartado 36
Merida
VENEZUELA

International Development Research Centre
PO Box 8500
Ottawa, Ontario K1G 3H9
CANADA

International Youth Federation (IYF)
Klostermollevej 46
Skanderborg DK 8660
DENMARK

Alexander Sergeevich Isaev
State Committee for Forests
Novocheremushkinskaya
Moscow 59
RUSSIAN FEDERATION

Hiroyuki Ishi
Asahi Shimbun
5-3-2 Isukiji, Chuo-ku
Tokyo
JAPAN

Island Resources Foundation
Red Hook Centre, PO Box 33
St. Thomas USVI 00802
BARBADOS

David Edward James
13 Rayner Road
Whale Beach 2107
AUSTRALIA

Roger James
Central Television
46 Charlotte Street
London W1
UNITED KINGDOM

Gochoogin Jamts
Chief of the Society "Our Mother Nature"
Editorial Office, "Ardyn Erkhe"
Ulaanbaatar -12
MONGOLIA

Zhang Jia-Shun
Anbui
Yingshang County
CHINA

Peter Jones
Natural History Unit
Broadcasting House, Whiteladies Road
Bristol B58 2LR
UNITED KINGDOM

Dr. Peter Jovanovic
Association of Scientific Unions
8 Omladinskih Brigada
Beograd 11070
SERBIA

Shecou-Bah Kabbah
2 Second Bongay Street
Freetown
SIERRA LEONE

Yolanda Kakabadse
UNCED
PO Box 80
CH-1231 Conches
SWITZERLAND

Luis Sumar Kalinowski
Avenida de la Infancia
No. 440
Huanchac
Cusco
PERU

Hayrettin Karaca
Samanli Koy
Yalova 81887
TURKEY

Abdullahi Karani
National Range Agency
PO Box 1759
Mogadishu
SOMALIA

G. V. and K. Karlekar
Calcutta Social Project
172/3 Rashbehari Avenue
Calcutta 700029
INDIA

Mohamed Kassas
Faculty of Science
University of Cairo
Giza
EGYPT

Milton M. Kaufmann
Monitor International
191102 Roman Way
Gaithersburg, MD
USA

Kerala Sastra Sahitya Parishad (KSSP)
Anayara
Trivandrum 695 029
INDIA

Robert Glenn Ketchum
696 Stone Canyon Road
Los Angeles, CA 90077
USA

Aila Inkero Keto
15 Colorado Avenue
Bardon 4065
AUSTRALIA

Mugamir Eisa Khalifa
c/o Dr. El Hag El-Tayeb
El-Tahir
PO Box 1975
Khartoum
SUDAN

Shoaib Sultan Khan
The Aga Khan Rural Support
Programme
Babar Road, PO Box 506
Gilgit, Northern Areas
PAKISTAN

Ashok Khosla
22 Olf Plame Marg
New Delhi 57
INDIA

Sophie Kiarie
The Bellerive Foundation
PO Box 8, Ruiru
Nairobi
KENYA

Philip Rivogbe Kio
Forestry Research Institute of Nigeria
PMB 5054
Ibadan
NIGERIA

Kitakyushu City
1-1 Jonai, Fukuoka Prefecture Kokura
Kita District
JAPAN

Roberto Klein
Avenida Sete de Setembro, 547
Itajai SC 88 300
BRAZIL

Oliver Henry Knowles
Mineracao Rio de Norte S.A.
Caixa Postal 23
Porto Trombetas
Cep. 68275 Para
BRAZIL

Sook Pyo Kwon
300-77 Echon Dong Youg
San Ky
Seoul
REPUBLIC OF KOREA

Alphonse Lafontaine
University Catholique
Louvain
BELGIUM

Dr. Fernando Ranjen Lalith
Wildlife & Nature Protection Society of Sri Lanka
Chaitya Road, Marine Drive
1 Colombo
SRI LANKA

Hugh F. Lamprey
Littlewide Field Farm
Inwardleigh, Oakhampton
Exeter EX20 3DA
UNITED KINGDOM

Thomas Landgren
Asgatan 6
S-54700 Gullspang
SWEDEN

Winfried Lang
Ambassador, Permanent Mission of Austria
7-9, rue de Varembe
Geneva CH-1211
SWITZERLAND

Geoffrey Lean
The Observer
London
UNITED KINGDOM

Philippe Lebreton
Beynost
Miribel F-01700
FRANCE

Sietz A. Leeflang
De Bleken 2
Boxtel 5282 HB
THE NETHERLANDS

Leichtmetall-Gessellschaft mbH (LMG)
Sulterkamp 71
Essen 11 D-4300
GERMANY

Pierre Lequeux
Commission of the European Communities
20 Chemin du Tour
Soignies 7400
BELGIUM

Les Amis De La Terre
38, Rue Meslay
Paris 75003
FRANCE

Dean R. Lindo
Government of Belize
Buttonwood Estate
Belize City
BELIZE

Dr. U.B. Lindstrom
Finnish Committee for UNICEF
Perttulantie 6
SF 00210 Helsinki
FINLAND

Joseph T. Ling
2090 Arcade Street
St. Paul, MN 55117
USA

Guy Lionnet
PO Box 68
Mahe
SEYCHELLES

Andrew and Katie Lipkis
12601 Mulholland Drive
Beverly Hills, CA 90210
USA

George Livanos
Hellenic Marine Environment Protection Association
5 Pergamon Street
Nea Smyrni
Athens
GREECE

Dr. Bindu N. Lohani
Asian Development Bank
2330 Roxas Boulevard
1300 Manila
PHILIPPINES

Thomas E. Lovejoy
Smithsonian Institution
8526 Georgetown Pike
McLean, VA 22102
USA

James Lovelock
Coombe Mill
St. Giles on the Heath
Launceston PL159RY
UNITED KINGDOM

Magazine of the Czech Union for Nature Conservation
NIKA - Editor's Office
Slezska 9
120 29 Praba 2
Vinobrady
CZECHOSLOVAKIA

King Mahendra Trust for Nature Conservation
Babar Mahal, PO Box 3712
Kathmandu
NEPAL

Susan Mahon
Barbados Environmental Association
PO Box 132
Bridgetown
BARBADOS

Jom Malai
Tha-Sadei Bird Conservation Unit
Maung District
Supunburi 7200
THAILAND

Malayan Nature Society
17 Jalan SS2/53,
47300 Petaling Jaya Selangor
MALAYSIA

Torsten Malmberg
Human Ecology Division
University of Lund
PO Box 117
221 00 Lund
SWEDEN

Pierre Malychef
Sahel's Pharmacy
Jal-el-Dib
LEBANON

Igor Mann
PO Box 20360
Nairobi
KENYA

Abdel Wahab Marakchi
CRDA de Kairouan 3100
Kairouan
TUNISIA

Marevivo
Viale G Cesare 14
Rome 00192
ITALY

Nicos Margaris
Kitheronos 39
Chalandri 152 35
GREECE

Uri Marinov
Director General, Ministry for the Environment
PO Box 6234
Jerusalem 91061
ISRAEL

Gladys Khangwayini Mashinini
Ecolink
PO Box 727
White River 1240
SOUTH AFRICA

Mathare Youth Sports Association (MYSA)
PO Box 69038
Nairobi
KENYA

Peter Matthiessen
Bridge Lane
Sagaponack
New York, NY 11962
USA

Elizabeth May
52 Pinchurt
Ottawa, Ontario
CANADA

J. Michael McCloskey
Sierra Club
408 C Street, NE
Washington, DC 20002
USA

Colleen McCrory
Box 93
New Denver
British Columbia
CANADA

Shirley McGreal
International Primate Protection League
PO Box 766
Summerville, SC 29484
USA

Dr. Donald McMichael
244 La Perouse Street
Canberra 2603
AUSTRALIA

Dr. David McTaggart
Greenpeace
Via Sassone, 1
Paciano 06060
ITALY

Margaret Mee
Norman James Melrose
Nyamanyoke Farm
PO Box 37
Mhangwa
ZIMBABWE

Ambassador Mateo Margarinos de Mello
URUGUAY

Chico Mendes Foundation
c/o Allegretti Institute for Amazonic Studies Rua Itupava 1220
Curitiba Parana 80.040
BRAZIL

Anna H. Merz
Ngare Sergoi Rhino Sanctuary
c/o Lewa Downs
PO Isiolo
KENYA

Bruno Messerli
Universitat Bern
Hallerstrasse 12
Bern CH-3012
SWITZERLAND

Wlodzimierz Michajlow
Noakowskiego Street 14
(Apt 11)
Warsaw WO-666
POLAND

Claude Michel
MAURITIUS

Christine Milne
Green Independents
RSD 402, Castra Road
Ulverstone 7315
AUSTRALIA

Dr. Veer Bhadra Mishra
Tulsi Mandir
Tulsi Ghat
Varanasi
Uttar Pradesh
INDIA

Daniel Arap Moi
President of Kenya
State House
Nairobi
KENYA

Harekala Moideen
Kisan Nagar
Harekala Post and Village
Mangalore DK
INDIA

Dr. Mario J. Molina
Deparment of EAPS
MIT, 54-1312
Cambridge, MA 02139
USA

Edgardo Mondolfi
Longonot Place No. 57
Harry Thuku Road
Nairobi
KENYA

Raul Montenegro
FUNAM
Casilla de Correo 83
Correo Central
Cordoba 5000
ARGENTINA

Brian Morton
University of Hong Kong
7B, 23 Sha Wan Drive
HONG KONG

Maureen Mosley
Oak Meadow School
PO Box 1003
Ojai, CA 93023
USA

Hasna J. Moudud
159 Gulshan Avenue
Dhaka
BANGLADESH

Josip Movcan
48231 Plitvicka Jezera
YUGOSLAVIA

Tom Muller
Department of Research
Ministry of Agriculture
PO Box 8100, Causeway
Harare
ZIMBABWE

Ahmad Abu Musa
Baa'th Pioneer
PO Box 2638
Damascus
SYRIA

Norman Myers
Upper Meadow
Old Road
Headington, Oxford
OX3 9AP
UNITED KINGDOM

Fundacion Natura
Av 6 de Diciembre 5053 y el Comercio
PO Box 243
Quito
ECUADOR

Natural Resources
Defense Council (NRDC)
1350 New York Avenue, NW
Suite 300
Washington, DC 20005
USA

Nature Conservancy
International
1800 North Kent Street
Suite 800
Arlington, VA 22209
USA

National Geographic Society
1145 17th Street, NW
Washington, DC 20036
USA

National Mobilization Programme
(NMP)
Government of Ghana
Accra
GHANA

Mark Dokotela Ncube
Dept of Natural Resources
PO Box 132
Gwanda
ZIMBABWE

Pamuchigere Nembire
Pfura District Council Natural
Resources Comm
Nembire School, PO Box 9060
Centenary
ZIMBABWE

Nigerian Conservation Foundation
No. 5 Wesley Road
Ikoyi
Lagos
NIGERIA

Nyakinyua Gitiri Women's Group
PO Box 89, Kahuro
Murang'a
KENYA

Nyamunda Nyamuniwa
Musamhi School
Private Bag 520
Mutoko
ZIMBABWE

Michael A. N. Odula
Tom Mboya High School
Rusinga Island, PO Box 13
Mbita
KENYA

Shigeyuki Okajima
The Yomiuri Simbun
The 1-7-1 Ohtemachi
Chiyodaku
Tokyo
JAPAN

Perez Olindo
Wildlife Conservation and
Management Department
PO Box 40241
Nairobi
KENYA

Joseph R. O'Neal
PO Box 35, Road Town
Tortola
BRITISH VIRGIN ISLANDS

ONERN
Los Petirrojos 355
El Palomar, San Isidro
Lima
PERU

OPIRG
Suite 201
455 Spadina Avenue
Toronto, Ontario
CANADA

Maria Teresa Ortiz
c/o Conservation
International
1015 18th Street NW
Suite 1000
Washington, DC 20036
USA

Adama Ouedraogo
NAAM/SIX 'S'
BP 100
Ouahigouya
BURKINA FASO

Bernard Ledea Ouedraogo
BP 100
Ouahigouya
BURKINA FASO

Gunavantrai Oza
Oza Building, Salatwada
Baroda 390 001
INDIA

Paasban/Family Planning Association
3-A, Temple Road
Lahore 54000
PAKISTAN

Paulinho Paiakan
Brasilia
BRAZIL

The Hon. Geoffrey Palmer
72 Elizabeth Street
Mount Victoria
Wellington 2
NEW ZEALAND

Krishna Kumar Pandey
4/80 Jawalakhel
GPO Box 3226
Kathmandu
NEPAL

Chang-Keun Park
265-216 Hongeun
3-Dong Sudaemun-Ku
Seoul
REPUBLIC OF KOREA

Karl Partsch
Bei Kohler
8971 Siegeswang 33
Post ofterschwang
GERMANY

Pisit Na Patalung
Wildlife Fund - Thailand
255 Soi Asoke, Sukhumvit 21
Bangkok 10110
THAILAND

Roger Payne
Whale and Dolphin Conservation
Society
191 Weston Road
Lincoln, MA 01773
USA

Dr. David Pearce
90 Kimbolton Road
Bedford MK40 2PE
UNITED KINGDOM

Nancy Pearlman
Educational Communications
PO Box 35473
Los Angeles, CA 90035
USA

Senator Claiborne Pell
Senate Office Building
335 Russell
Washington, DC 20510
USA

Pemasky - Kuna Wildlands Project
Apartado 2012, Paraiso
Ancon
PANAMA

Basil Peskov
V-Kasiovka St. II-5
Moscow 125083
RUSSIAN FEDERATION

Philippine Foundation of Rural Broadcasters
4th Floor, National Irrigation
Administration Building
E. de los Santos Avenue
Diliman
Quezon City
PHILLIPINES

Association Nationale Des Pioniers Des Reboisement
BP 10508
Dakar-Liberte
SENEGAL

Carlos Pizani
Corporacion Nacional Forestal
(CONAF)
Casilla 317
Vina del Mar
CHILE

Pokret Gorana Srbije
Rankeova 17
Belgrade 11000
YUGOSLAVIA

Nicholas Polunin
Foundation for Environmental
Conservation
7 Chernin Taverney
1218 Grand-Saconnex
Geneva
SWITZERLAND

Phra Ajahn Pongsak
Wat Phalad
Humbon Sudhep
Mueng District
Ching Mai 5000
THAILAND

Population and Community Development Association
8 Sukhumvit 12
Bangkok 10110
THAILAND

Jonathan Porritt
Friends of the Earth
26-28 Underwood Street
London EC 1
UNITED KINGDOM

Dr. Suryo Wardhoyo Prawiroatmodjo
Enviromental Education Centre (PPLH)
Jl. Undaan Kulon 43
Surabaya 60274
Jawa-Timur
INDONESIA

Progressio-Programa Agroforestal
Alianza del Campesino con el Arbol
Avda. Maximo Gomez
27 de Febrero, Piso 3
Santo Domingo Apartado Postal 22036
DOMINICAN REPUBLIC

Pronatura
c/o RosaVillamayor
Dpto Parques Nacionales y Monumentos
Historicos, Ministerio de Defensa Nacional
Asuncion
PARAGUAY

Dina Iosifovna Protsenko
Ukrainian Committee on Environmental Protection
Sadovaya Street 3
Kiev
THE UKRAINE

Public Broadcasting Service
475 L'enfant Plaza, SW
Washington, DC 20074-2117
USA

Maritza Pulido-Santana
Environmental Education Programs
Institutional de Parques, Aptado 76471
Caracas 107 A
VENEZUELA

Barbara Pyle
International Documentary Unit, Turner Broadcasting
2630 Dobbs Circle NSW
Atlanta, GA 30327
USA

Quercus Associacao
R. Trindade Coelho - IC - 4o
4000 Porto
PORTUGAL

Vo Quy
Centre for Natural Resources Management and Environmental Studies (CRES)
Hanoi University
19 Le Thanh Tong Street
Hanoi
VIETNAM

Gabor Racz
c/o National Authority for Environment Protection
V/Arany Janos u. 25-1051
Budapest 1365
HUNGARY

G. Radhamohan
Qrs No DS-4/4
MLA Colony, Unit-4
Bhubaneswar 571001
INDIA

Charlotte Rajeriarison
c/o Jules Frippiat
UNDP, Rue Rainitovo, BP. 1348
Antananarivo
MADAGASCAR

Alegria Fonseca de Ramiriz
Fundacion Alma
Calle 100 No. 11B-95 Oficina 201
Santafe de Bogota
COLOMBIA

M. K. Ranjitsinh
Ministry of Environment, Gov't of India
Paryavaran Bhawan, CGO Complex, 4th Floor,
New Delhi 110 003
INDIA

Valentin Rasputin
Irkutsk
RUSSIAN FEDERATION

Peter H. Raven
Missouri Botanical Garden
St. Louis, MO 63166
USA

Robert Redford
Institute for Resource Management
19 Exchange Place
Salt Lake City, UT
USA

Terence Evezard Reilly
PO Box 33
Mbabane
SWAZILAND

Raulino Reitz
PO Box 30
Itapema-SC 88220
BRAZIL

Iosefatu Reti
Head of Government Office
Government of Western Samoa
Apia
WESTERN SAMOA

Fiona Reynolds
Council for the Protection of Rural England
16 The Crescent
London E17
UNITED KINGDOM

Chae Shik Rho
89-2 Neung-Dong
Seoul
REPUBLIC OF KOREA

Yung-Hee Rho
Graduate School of Environmental Studies
Seoul National University, 56-1 Sinim-Dong
Seoul, 151-742
REPUBLIC OF KOREA

Robert Richter
Robert Richter Productions
330 West 42nd Street
New York, NY 10036
USA

Margaret Robertson
The Wilderness Society
57 Liverpool Street
Sydney 2000
AUSTRALIA

Anita Roddick
The Body Shop Ltd
Littlehampton
Sussex NB17 7LR
UNITED KINGDOM

Park Ro-Kyeong
202-19 Dai Jo Dong
Eonpyeong Gu
Seoul
REPUBLIC OF KOREA

Celso Roque
The Haribon Foundation
3rd Floor/Liberty Building
835 Pasay Road
Makati, Metro Manila
PHILIPPINES

Basil Rossi
Prosamapi
Palestina, Camarines Sur
Bicol Bioregion
PHILIPPINES

Felix Yakovlevich Rovinsky
Institute of Global Climate & Ecology
20B Glebovskaya Street
Moscow 107258
RUSSIAN FEDERATION

Dr. Sherwood F. Rowland
University of California
Department of Chemistry
Irvine, CA 92717
USA

Veronica Irene Joy Royes
4 Claremont Avenue
Kingston 6
JAMAICA

Rius and Tiahoga Ruge
Consejo Nacional para
la Cultura y las Artes
Jaime Nuno 77 Guadalupe Inn
CP 01020
MEXICO

Rauno Ruuhijarvi
Department of Botany,
University of Helsinki
Fabianinkatu 24A
Helsinki 00100
FINLAND

Felix Augustine Ryan
8 West Mada Street
Srinagar Colony
Saidapet - 15
Madras 400015
INDIA

Omda Sabil
c/o Dr. Ahmad Ibrahim
Regional Ministry of Agriculture
Dar Fur el Fasher
SUDAN

Mohammed Saeed Al-Haffar
Environmental Studies Unit
Qatar University
PO Box 2713
QATAR

Saenaua Women's Association
Anoasa Village West Kwara'ae
Malaita Province
SOLOMON ISLANDS

Sahabat Alam Malaysia (SAM)
37 Lorong Birch
Penang
MALAYSIA

Jose Manuel Salazar
Departamento del Risaralda
Carrera 7 No. 8-05
Marsella
COLOMBIA

Pablo Ruuhijarvi Sanchez
Universidad Tecnica de Cajamarca
Cajamarca
PERU

Silvia Sanchez
APECO
Parque Jose de Acosta 187
Magdalena, Lima 17
PERU

Dr. Richard Sandbrook
IIED
3 Endsleigh Street
London WCl 11 ODD
UNITED KINGDOM

M.A. Partha Sarathy
IUCN Commission for Education and Training
Hamsimi, 1 12th Cross
Raymahal Vilas Ext
560-080 Bangalore
INDIA

Victoria Satiriadou
Prime Minister's Office Davaki 73
Papagon
Athens
GREECE

Dr. Taishichiro Satoh
Japan Wildlife Research Center
3-39-12, Hongo
Bunkyo-ku
100 Tokyo
JAPAN

Klaus Scharmer
Dohrer Weg 2
Julich D-5170
GERMANY

Anesia do Amaral Schimidt
Caixa Postal, 287
Campinas SP
BRAZIL

Pierre Schram
81 route de Longwy
Bertrange L8080
LUXEMBOURG

Leonard Schwartz
Rainforest Action Alliance
450 Christian Herald Road
Valley Cottage, NY 10989
USA

Colette Serruya
Israel Oceanographic and
Limnological Research Inc.
PO Box 8030
Haifa
ISRAEL

Roque Sevilla
Whymper 1210
Casilla No. 21-443
Quito
ECUADOR

Seychelles Islands Foundation
Independence House
Mahe
SEYCHELLES

Philip Shabecoff
The New York Times
229 West 43rd Street
New York, NY
USA

Kantilal Jivan Shah
PO Box 699
Mahe
SEYCHELLES

Mukhtar Shakhanoy
480002 7 Lenin prs
Alma-Ata
KAZAKHSTAN

Shanglijia Village
Ningbo
Beijing
Jing County
PEOPLE'S REPUBLIC OF CHINA

Sawroop Krishna Sharma
Environment Society of Chandigarh
Karuna Sadan, Sector 11-B
Chandigarh 160 011
INDIA

Mary Sheehy
103 Balloonagh Estate
Tralee
Kerry,
IRELAND

Daphne Marjorie Sheldrick
David Sheldrick Wildlife Trust
Box 15555
Nairobi
KENYA

Jill Sheppard
Bush Hill, The Garrison
St. Michael
BARBADOS

Eung-Bai Shin
Hanyang University
#10 264-454 Limun 2-Dong
Tongdaemoon-Gu
Seoul 130-082
REPUBLIC OF KOREA

Li Shuangliang
Taiyuan Iron and Steel Plant
Taiyuan, Shanxi Province
PEOPLE'S REPUBLIC OF CHINA

Andrew Augustus Simmons
JEMS Institute for Popular Education
Enhams
Prospect Post Office
ST. VINCENT AND THE
GRENADINES

Mary Simon
Inuit Circumpolar Conference
650 32nd Ave, Suite 404
Lachine, Quebec H8T 3K4
CANADA

John Sinclair
36 Kemp Street
Gladesville 2111
AUSTRALIA

Thodoros Skoulikidis
Dexamenis 10
Politia 145 63
GREECE

Snake in the Grass Moving Theatre
4131 Garry Street
Richmond BC VZE 2T9
CANADA

Ben Soans
GG Soans Memorial Peoples
Van Vigyan Kendras, Siragate,
Tumkur
Karnataka State 572106
INDIA

Society for the Protection of Nature in Israel
4 Hashfela Street
Tel Aviv, 66183
ISRAEL

Otto Soemarwoto
Padjadjaran University
21 JL Iman Bonjol
Bandung
INDONESIA

Vladimir Evgenievich Sokolov
USSR Academy of Science
Leninsky Prosp. 33
Moscow
RUSSIAN FEDERATION

Chodchoy Sophonpanich
Environmental Awareness Promotion Group
333 Silom Road
Bangkok 10500
THAILAND

Southern Women Against Toxics
101 West Monroe Street
PO Drawer 1526
Livingston, AL 35470
USA

Herbert Jose de Souza
IBASE
Vincente de Souza St, 29 Botofogo
Rio de Janeiro 22251
BRAZIL

James G. Speth
World Resources Institute
1735 New York Avenue, NW Suite 400
Washington, DC 20006
USA

Irina Vasilevna Springuel
Aswan University
Faculty of Science
Aswan
EGYPT

Sri Lanka Enviromental Journalists Forum (SLEJF)
PO Box 26
434/4 Sri Jayawardenapura
Colombo
SIR LANKA

Starkist Seafood Company
180 East Ocean Boulevard
Long Beach, CA 90082
USA

Stichting Werkgroep Behoud Tropisch Regenwo
c/o Ministry of Environment
The Hague
THE NETHERLANDS

Marion Stoddart
PO Box 200
Groton, MA 01450
USA

Bjoern Strandli
Stotrigveien 40
1560 Harkollen
NORWAY

Maurice Strong
UNCED Secretariat
4 Chemin de Conches
Conches 1213
SWITZERLAND

Godofredo Stutzin
CODEFF
Camino El Alto
Santiago
CHILE

Dr. David Suzuki
Department of Zoology
University of British Colombia
Vancouver V6T 1W5
CANADA

Robert Swan
Project Earth
1700 K Street, NW
Suite 1200
Washington, DC 20006
USA

Sayyid Shabib Bin Taimour
Ministry of Environment
PO Box 323
Muscat
OMAN

Bassirou Tall
Grand Yoff
Quartier Leona Villa 102
Dakar BP 10201
SENEGAL

Krisna Tamrakar
Radio Nepal
Cha-1-9 Gavrighat
Kathmandu
NEPAL

Anna Maria Rosa Teixeira
Rua Marques do Angeja 150
Alcabideche
Estoril 2765
PORTUGAL

Peter Thacher
World Resources Institute
1735 New York Avenue NW
Washington, DC 20006
USA

The Hon. Margaret Thatcher
Parliament House
London
UNITED KINGDOM

Ven Kirantidiye Pannasekera Thero
Upper Mahawelly Environment
Development Pr
Doragala
Ramboda
SRI LANKA

Pravit Thomyavit
Thai Yuwa Kasetkorn
Promotion Foundation
2143/1 Phaholyothin Road
Bangkben
Bangkok
THAILAND

Normita Thongtham
10/1 Soi Prasartsuk
Yen-Akard Road
Tung Mahamek
Bangkok 10120
THAILAND

Sir Crispin Tickell
Green College
University of Oxford
Oxford
UNITED KINGDOM

Jon Tinker
Panos Institute
8 Alfred Place
London WC1E ZEB
UNITED KINGDOM

George H. Tomlinson
920 Perrot Boulevard
Ile Perrot, Quebec
CANADA

Sione Latuila Tongilava
PO Box 5
Nuku'alofa
TONGA

Edward L. Towle
Island Resources Foundation
Red Hook Centre, PO Box 33
St. Thomas USVI 00802
BARBADOS

Foune Traore
c/o Minister of State for Rural Development
Boite Postale 4055
Dakar
SENEGAL

Turkish Association for Conservation of Nature and Natural Resources
Menekse Sokak no 29/4
Kizilay Ankara
TURKEY

Jun Ui
Okinawa University
982 Kokuba, Naha
Okinawa 902
JAPAN

The Una Emeralds Society
Brace Zardin 1
Bihac 77000
CROATIA

NGO/UN Cooperation Forum
JL Gaharu I/VIA, Cipete
Jakarta Selatan
INDONESIA

UNEPCOM (USSR Commission for UNEP)
GKNT, 11 Gorky Street
K-9 Moscow 103905
RUSSIAN FEDERATION

UNESCO Club of the University of Yaounde
BP 337 - S/G Club UNESCO
Yaounde
CAMEROON

Tsitsi Vangili
64 Selous Avenue/Seventh Street
PO Box UA339
Harare
ZIMBABWE

Sr. Maria Aida Velasquez
Lingkod Tao-Kaliksan
PO Box 2734
Manila 1099
PHILIPPINES

Josef Velek
Dobrovskeho 14
Praha 7 17000
CZECHOSLOVAKIA

Vlassi Vellopoulos
Assimaki Fotila St. 99
Patras
GREECE

Lily Venizelos
3 Merlin Street
Athens GR 106 71
GREECE

Richard A. Vollenweider
National Water Research Institute
PO Box 5050
Burlington, Ontario L7R 4A6
CANADA

Valentin V. Voloshin
Presidium of the Ukrainian Academy of Science
Vladimirskaya Street 54
Kiev
THE UKRAINE

Aminata Wade
c/o Association des Soeurs-Unies contre le Desert
11 Avenue Briere de L'Isle
Dakar
SENEGAL

Joe Walulya-Mukasa
PO Box 1684
Jinja
UGANDA

W. M. U. Wanigasundara
A 3/1 Government Flats
Hospital Road
Dehiwala
SRI LANKA

Stepen S. Wanje
Rural Life Extension, Fudumi
PO Box 200
Maragoli
KENYA

Dr. Robert T. Watson
Office of Space Science & Communications
NASA Headquarters
Washington, DC 20546
USA

David Alexander Weir
526 Northern Avenue
Mill Valley, CA 94941
USA

Michael Werikhe
c/o East African Wildlife Society
PO Box 20110
Nairobi
KENYA

Arthur H. Westing
Westing Associates
RFD 1, Box 919
Putney, VT 05346
USA

Gilbert F. White
Institute of Behavioral Sciences 6
University of Colorado, PO Box 482
Boulder, CO 80304
USA

Wildlife Clubs of Kenya
PO Box 40658
Nairobi
KENYA

Vivian John Wilson
Chipangali Wildlife Orphanage
PO Box 1057
Bulawayo
ZIMBABWE

David Wingate
10 Elm Lodge
Harbour Road
Warwick
BERMUDA

Paul Winter
PO Box 72
Litchfield, CT 06759
USA

Erna Witoelar
Jalan Cidurian 39
Jakarta 12170
INDONESIA

Women of Mupata Village
Matsa Store, Mupata Village
PO Box 119
Gutu
ZIMBABWE

World Assembly of Youth (WAY)
Ved Bellahoj 4, 2700 Bronshoj
Copenhagen
DENMARK

World Association of Girl Guides and Girl Scouts
World Bureau
Olave Centre, 12c Lyndhurst Road
London NW3 5PQ
UNITED KINGDOM

World Organisation of the Scout Movement
Rue du Pre-Jerome 5, Case Postale 78
Geneva 4 CH-1211
SWITZERLAND

Worldwide Fund for Nature (WWF)
Ch. de Haes, Avenue du Mont Blanc
Gland CH-1196
SWITZERLAND